THE TRINITY STORY

— I —

IN THE BEGINNING

The Trinity Story – In the Beginning
https://thetrinitystory.com

First edition, 2021

Published by
Trinity Publishing House
https://trinitypublishinghouse.com
ISBN 978-619-91938-0-8

Text copyright © 2021 L. H. Found, Ventsislav Stoykov
Illustrations copyright © 2021 Hari Atanasov, Penka Atanasova
Editing and proofreading: Alexa Tewkesbury
Design and typesetting: Ivaylo Atanasov

Printed and bound in Bulgaria

L. H. FOUND

AND

VENTSISLAV STOYKOV

THE TRINITY STORY

IN THE BEGINNING

TRINITY PUBLISHING HOUSE

To my precious daughters –
Danya, Margarita and Aurora.
May you find the pearl of great price
and may your lives be a living testimony
of the Lord Jesus
and of His great love for us.

L. H. Found

◻◻◻

To my wife, my children
and their future children.

Ventsislav Stoykov

Contents

The Trinity Story uses icons
to represent the different characters in the book,
with the icon placed to the left of the words
spoken by the respective character.
Here is a key to the icons and the characters
they symbolise in this book:

The Trinity

The Father

The Son

The Holy Spirit

Michael

Gabriel

Heylel

Adam

Eve

Satan

CHAPTER

Before the World Began

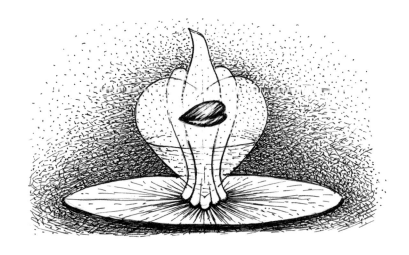

The Trinity

◈ Everyone has a story to tell but there is a story that started before all others – one that was the beginning. It is this story that I'd like to share with you because I am the One who has seen it unfold and who has taken part in it every step of the way. Who are you? – I hear you ask. I am the One who has spoken to you in many ways before, even though at times you didn't recognise My voice or understand what I wanted to say. That's right – I am God. My story has been told so many times and in so many ways but not quite in the way I am about to tell it now.

I know everything about you, and I'd like you to learn about Me. But even more than that, I'd like you to get to know Me personally. A personal knowing of Me, however, cannot begin unless you first learn that I am not *a* person but *Persons*. That's right – I'm more than One Person. There are Three in Me and I am in Three: Three Persons, One God. So let Me introduce Myself. I am...

◈ the Father,

✝ the Son,

✤ and the Holy Spirit.

◈ When people found out that I am One God in Three Persons, they made up a word to help them understand and describe that characteristic of Mine:

◈ Tri

✝ ni

✤ ty.

♲ Trinity! It's actually two words made into one: the word "three" and the word "unity", because –

◈ I

ↀ am

♲ Three,

♲ yet One – a Unity of Three Persons. I'm a plural singularity and a singular plurality! I'm One Being – God – but in Three Persons – Father, Son and Holy Spirit. Now that you know this about Me, you can get to know each of My Persons individually. Meet the Holy Spirit first, as He is the first Person people in the world encounter when they connect to Me.

The Holy Spirit

♲ I'm the Holy Spirit. People don't usually know they encounter Me when they first turn to God as I don't draw attention to Myself. It's just not what I'm like. I'm holy, you see, which, as you'll find out, means that there are things and actions that are completely foreign to My nature and My preferences. As a Person, I'm someone who always points people to the Son; the Son of God. That's what I'm constantly doing and that's how you will know that I, the Holy Spirit, am the One speaking to you. I turn people's attention towards the Son by revealing His glory, His majesty, His beauty and all the wonderful things about Him. You see, it's all about the Son, as you will learn through this book. The story of the Son is the most wonderful, the most exciting and the most

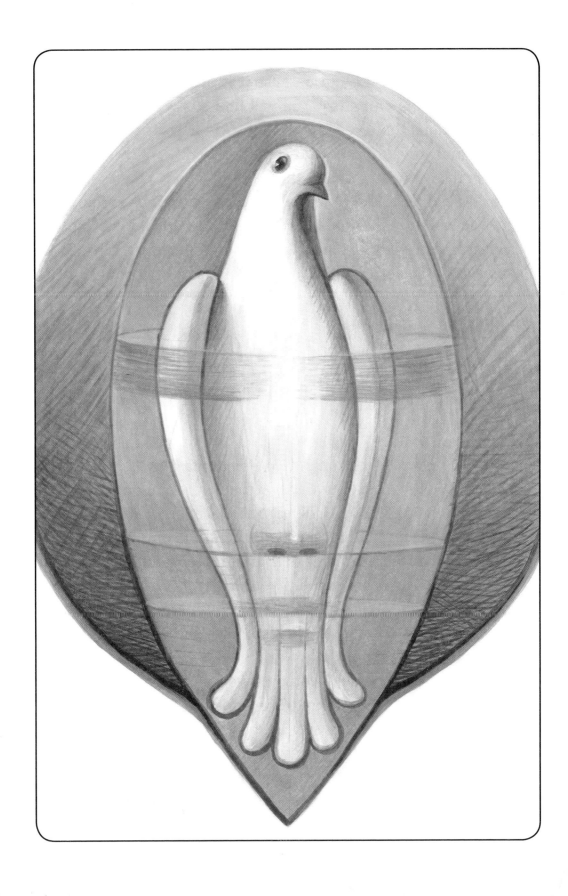

important story ever told because it is also the story of the world. Reading Our story, you will find answers to some of the questions that everyone in the world is asking, such as: "How and why did the world come to exist?", "Why is there evil in the world and what is the solution?" and "Where is the world heading to?" The answer to these questions is found in One Person – the One I always point to – the Son of God. Now that you've heard Me speak about Him, why not listen to what He has to say about Himself? He's right here next to Me, as He always is.

The Son

῀῁ I'm here – the Son of God. It's so good to see you! As the Holy Spirit says, everything in the world is about Me. In getting to know Me, you will learn things about yourself and the world you live in that you couldn't learn in any other way. Not only will you get answers to those important questions the Holy Spirit mentioned but you will even get answers to questions you didn't know you had. That's because all things were made for Me and all things hold together in Me. If it were not for Me, the whole world would just crumble into nothingness. Of course, I wouldn't ever allow that to happen because I love the world and I love My Father who gave it to Me. He's always been and always will be My Father and I've always been and always will be His Son. The way the Holy Spirit points to Me and is always telling people about Me is the way I point to the Father and tell people all about

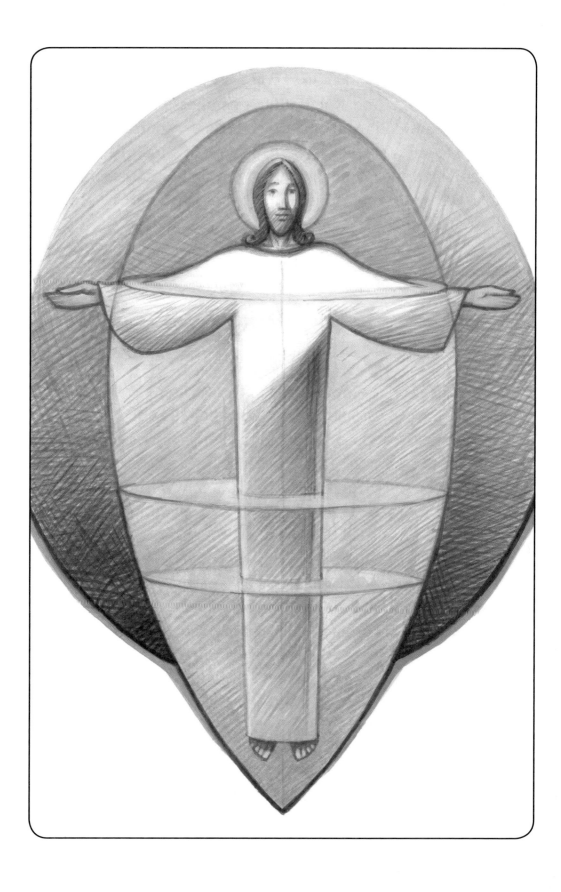

Him. What's the Father like, you ask? Well... He is just... WONDERFUL... too wonderful! It's impossible for you to see Him, know Him and understand Him by yourself, but as you get to know Me, you'll come to know Him too. He makes it possible for people to know Him through Me, His Son, as He chooses to reveal Himself in Me. But why not meet Him yourself?

The Father

⊛ Dear ones – I am the Father. Just as My Son told you, We have always been Father and Son, Son and Father. The way the Holy Spirit points to the Son is the way the Son points to Me. I am the Father because He is My Son and He is the Son because I am His Father. The Holy Spirit, however, proceeds from Me – that is He comes from within Me. He has always proceeded from Me and I have always had the joy of being the One from whom He comes. The Spirit has always been with Us and We have always been with Him. He is My Spirit and He is the Son's Spirit but He is also the Holy Spirit, for that is His name and that is His nature – it always has been and it always will be. The Holy Spirit is the Spirit of holiness.

I am everything the Son is and I am everything the Holy Spirit is, but I am not the Son and I am not the Spirit – I am the Father. What do You say, Holy Spirit?

♨ That's right. And I am everything the Son is and everything the Father is, but I am neither the Son nor the

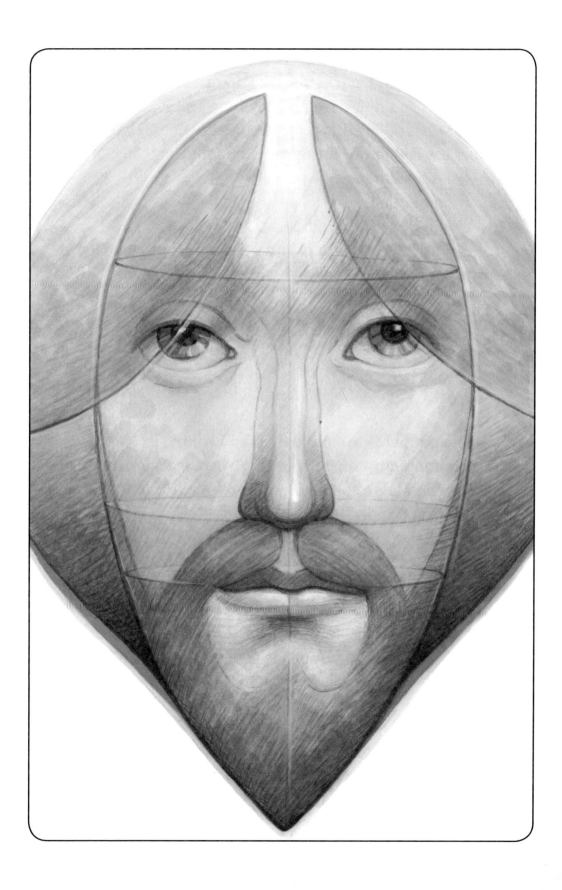

Father – I am the Holy Spirit. Isn't that right, Son?

⊕ You couldn't have put it better! The Father and the Spirit are everything that I am but they are not Me. And I am neither the Father nor the Spirit – I am the Son!

⊕ I, the Father

⊕ and I, the Son

⊕ and I, the Holy Spirit

⊕ am One God. I am Three Persons, but One God. I always have been and I always will be.

Love

⊕ Now that I've told you that I'm a trinity, let Me tell you another important thing about Me. There is something that flows within Me, from Father, to Son, to Spirit, to Father, to Son, to Spirit... and so on. You've heard this word many times. People in the world are constantly looking for this something, but not many grasp what it really means or what it is. It's the one thing everybody needs yet so few have known. Do you want to know what the name of this thing is? It's called Love. Love is not only what I do – it is who I am. I exist as an inseparable bond of respect, devotion and joy of being together in unity of thought, feeling, purpose and action. I, Father, Son and Holy Spirit am One Love. I am One God. I am Love. God is Love. I have always been and I always will be.

⊕ I love My Son and I love the Holy Spirit.

⊕ I love My Father and I love the Holy Spirit.

⊕ I love the Son and I love the Father.

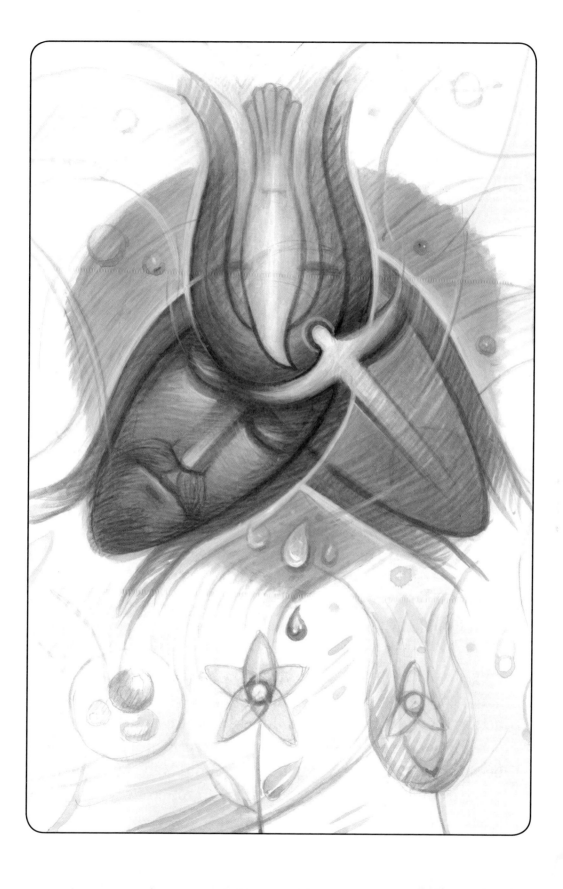

🔯 Our Love is the reason the world exists. It's all because of the Son.

🔥 I wanted to give My Son a gift that would show My love for Him in a special way.

🔥 And I wanted to be the One through whom that gift came.

🕇 It really was the best gift!

🔯 Yet before I tell you how all that happened, let Me first tell you more about Myself.

Holy

🔯 There is a characteristic of Mine that is almost as hard to explain as the fact that I'm a trinity and that I am Love, and that is that I'm holy. What this means is first that I am completely separate, different, above and beyond everything and everyone else – I have always been this way and I will always be. That's the reason why no one can ever fully understand Me. You see, to understand something new, people need to compare it to something they already know. For example, when someone wants to teach young children what the word "circle" means and what a circle looks like, they show them things that have that shape – an apple, the sun, people's eyes... In order to help people understand Me better, I compare Myself to things they are familiar with, yet in My essence I couldn't ever be described in this way because I am wholly, foundationally, completely, altogether other from all else. I'm in a category, a group of My own –

22

the God category – and comparison and similarity to Me can only exist within Me.

🜂 My Son and the Spirit are just like Me and I'm just like them.

🜁 I'm just like My Father and the Spirit and they're just like Me.

🜃 The Son and the Father are just like Me and I'm just like them.

🜨 Secondly, I am holy because of My character and My personality:

🜂 the things I like and the things I don't like;

🜁 the things I do and the things I don't do;

🜃 the way I am and the way I'm not.

🜨 I have been, I am and I always will be a certain way that can never and will never change. That's because there is nothing and no one outside Me that could ever affect, alter, influence, sway or change Me in any way whatsoever, and I Myself am devoted to being the way that I am. What this means is that the things I like and the things I don't like are constant and cannot be changed – there are things that are right in My eyes and things that are wrong, and nothing and no one could ever make them be another way.

🜂 My Son and the Spirit like the things I like,

🜁 and My Father and the Spirit like the things I like,

🜃 and the things I like are also liked by the Father and the Son!

🜨 So you see, I am

🜂 Holy,

🜁 Holy,

🜃 Holy!

Eternal

⊛ Let Me share with you another important thing about Me. You see, there's a reason why I say, "I always was and I always will be". Just like with the word "love", people use the word "always" without really understanding it. It's only when people get to know Me that they come to some understanding of what "always" means. That's because

⊕ I

⚕ am

🔥 eternal,

⊛ which means that I have always existed. I don't have a beginning, so I don't have an age. I'm timeless and ageless – I have lived forever and I will live forever and ever. This is hard for people to understand because everything in the world you live in has a beginning – a time when it came to exist in space. But I Myself am not like that. I don't live in time and space, but I do make Myself known within the time and space that people live in. I dwell in eternity – what can be called a never-ending "time and space", where My presence is enjoyed forever by those who come to live here.

Creator

⊛ I don't have a beginning, but I caused the beginning of everything that exists outside Me. You see, I Myself am the Creator of time and space and everything within them. There is nothing that began its existence without Me – everything was My idea, My design, My decision, My working and My completion. Everything came from Me when I was the only One who existed; when there was nothing else outside or apart from Me anywhere at any time. Everything that exists was first

⬙ My dream,

⛏ and My dream,

🔥 and Mine!

🕊 You see, all things you can see, and even things you can't see, first existed in the Father's heart. He is "the dreamer".

🔥 He is the One who usually gives the ideas...

⛏ ...and the ideas are always to do with pleasing Me, His Son.

⬙ I can't help it – My Son is everything to Me.

🔥 It's always My pleasure to take part in all of this.

The Dream

🕊 Let Me tell you about the greatest dream that I had in My heart. I once spoke:

⬙ Son, My heart is overflowing with love for You and the overflow looks like something. It looks like someone. A person. Persons. Humans. People...

⛏ I can see them too, Father. They're right here, hidden in My heart.

🔥 I also saw them, and I would love to call them into existence.

26

🜨 They will be for You, My Son. You are worthy of such a gift.

⛨ They will be Ours, Father. Mine

🔥 and Mine

🜨 and Mine.

The Reason

☸ That's how it happened. That's how it all began. It all started with the Father's dream. Everything I made first existed in My heart. That's where I saw you and your family, your life and your gifts, your dreams and your favourite things and places...

🜨 That's why it was easy for Me to make everything later because all I had to do was just look at the things that were already in My heart. Because the plan of creating people came from within My heart – they were My message of love for My Son. Before I even made them, I planned that they would eventually be brought as close to My heart as My Son is.

⛨ That they would know My Father the way I know Him; that they would know His love the way I know His love.

☸ That they would know Me – the Father, the Son and the Holy Spirit – and that we would spend eternity together. I *wanted* people. I desired to be with them for all eternity. I loved them with a love that would never end, even before I made a single one of them. I wanted love to be the reason we would live together, but not only My love for them – also their love for Me. I wanted them to freely love Me, the way I, Father, Son and Holy Spirit, have love within Myself.

Persons

⊕ Son, for people to be able to love Us, they would have to be like Us – in Our image, that is. Let Our image be the start of their existence but let them have a destination – an end, a goal... Let that goal be for them to become in Your likeness, My Son.

✝ In My likeness! That would be a fantastic journey for people to take together with Us.

🔥 I will help them on this journey of relationship with Us but first let's speak about how they will be in Our image.

⊕ Well, for one, We will make them persons like We are Persons. Persons with personalities... with characters... Beings who think, and want, and feel.

✝ Their ability to think and want and feel some will one day call the soul. Yet they will also have a part of them with which they will interact with Us that some will one day call the spirit.

🔥 Let's put these parts of humans together in one place – in a kind of home: the body. It will be the means through which they will interact with one another and with the outside world.

Physical Beings

🜂 The human body has to be different from that which makes up their inner being – it has to be altogether other...

🜊 Yes, their inner entities will be of one kind and the body of another... Let Us hear Your suggestion.

🜂 Let's make the human body a physical entity that lives in a physical world, while people's inner being will be non-physical. The physical world will also be called a material world and it will be made of matter – a substance that people will see with their eyes and touch with their hands. Let them also hear with their ears, smell with their noses, and taste with their tongues.

🜊 These will be their five physical senses. With them people will experience the material world, as matter will have various shapes, surfaces, densities and colours. The body's matter will be called flesh. The body will be the limit of each person – the outer part of people, and it will separate person from person, human from human, life from life.

🜕 People will only be able to exist in the physical world We make in a body. Through their bodies they will sense the material world, while the immaterial world they will sense through their immaterial parts. Thus, they will have both physical and non-physical senses. Let people's inner being be expressed through the body, so that their connection with Us and their thoughts, desires and feelings – the non-physical part of people – are shown and come to exist in the material world through their bodies.

🜂 So, they will use their bodies to communicate with Us and with one another, and through communication and interaction will build friendships, relationships and part-nerships.

Reproduction

☙ After deciding to make people to be in My image by making them persons with distinct and individual personalities, I planned on making them in My image in one other way. I said:

☙ Let's make people able to create life, to make other humans, other persons, who will also be in Our image. In this way people will make other people in Our image and give them life similar to the way We give life. The difference will be that people will need to use their bodies that We make for them to give life to others – that is to reproduce – while I create life where there is no life, and people where there are no people.

☙ So, let Us make people to be of two kinds: male people – men – and female people – women. Let men's and women's bodies be different and let them produce life when their bodies come together: male with female, one man with one woman.

☙ Each new person people make will be completely unique and individual, so that there won't be a single person who is exactly the same as another person! In this way We can have a friendship, a relationship, with each person who is completely unique and individual!

☙ Yes, each of them will have a life with Us and in Us

that will be special and unique and will be like no other life lived in relationship with Us.

A Family

🕈 Father, why don't We make people's bond with one another deeper?

🔥 Yes, why don't We make their connection not only a bond of the body, but also of the heart? Let Us make people part of a unity, part of a whole.

🌐 They will both be in My image and likeness, but men will reflect some parts and sides of Me better than women and women will reflect other parts and sides of Me better than men. Men and women will have different bodies and different minds and emotions but will not differ in that part of them that relates to the spiritual world. So, they will look different to one another, their feelings will be different, they will like and want different things, yet there won't be a distinction between men and women in the way they connect to Me...

🕈 The male and the female will be different and separate from one another yet One humanity, One relationship, One friendship, One family. Let's make the human family reflect Our love and let love be their connection – the thing that makes them One.

🔥 Let love be the reason they reproduce and make new humans – when the man becomes a father and the woman becomes a mother. Let the new humans the man and the woman make, be called their children – the male children boys and the female children girls.

🕊 A man and a woman will live together in a family because they love one another. Their love will cause them to prefer, lift up, give and surrender to one another in a way that reflects the way I, God – Father, Son and Holy Spirit – have love within Me. We always have loved one another,

🕊 We always do love one another

🔥 and We always will love one another.

🕊 When We make people to be in a family, they will reflect Us – separate persons in One unity – another way in which they will be in Our image. The family will be the relationship, the environment, in which people's children will grow up. The family unit will teach children who they are, how they can give and receive love, how they can use their creativity and what qualities they will need when they themselves become parents one day.

🕊 So, let the family be formed when one man and one woman come together in a bond that will be called "marriage" – a unique connection, an everlasting unity of love when the two will become one. When a man marries a woman, they will be pronounced husband and wife, words which will signify that they are now joined together in the bond of marriage, never to separate nor to join themselves to others.

🔥 And let them express their love for one another physically and thus produce children after expressing their love in becoming husband and wife, through the bond of marriage. So their physical connection will reflect the connection they have formed within their hearts.

🕊 Yes, let a man and a woman express their physical love for one another after they have devoted themselves

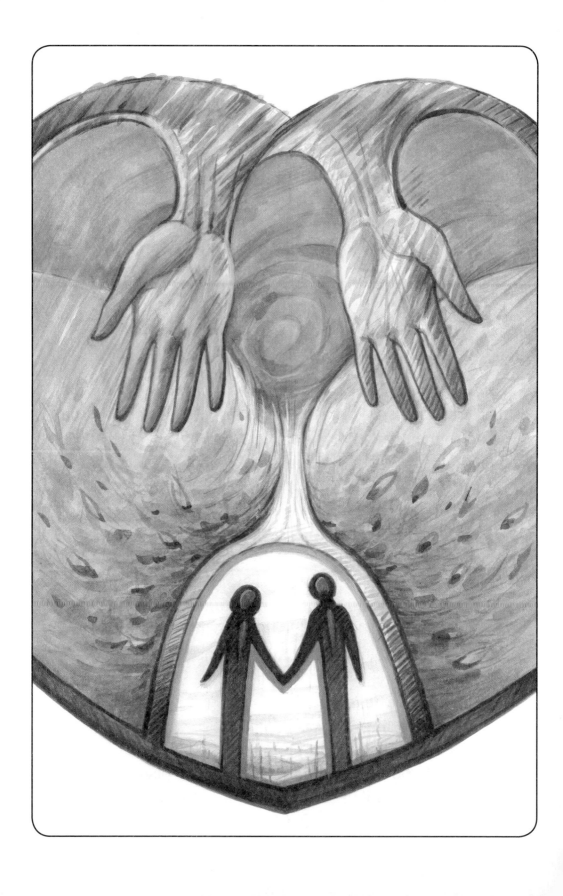

exclusively to one another through the bond of marriage. Let the expression of physical love strengthen their soul connection and let it be a powerful source of joy and pleasure for both the husband and the wife. Let every act of physical love between them be a renewal of their promise of eternal devotion to one another – a confirmation of their marriage bond.

Animals and Plants

⦿ As We will make people physical beings, let Us make their world physical too. Apart from people, let this physical world contain two other types of living things and let those living things exist in a set relationship with humanity and with one another.

⦿ Father, that's a great idea!

⦿ Yes, it's altogether marvellous!

⦿ Let's make the first type of beings also have physical bodies with five senses: sight, smell, touch, hearing and taste. Let them interact with the physical world through these bodies and let them also be able to reproduce. Let them have feelings and reasoning too, similar to those of humans. They will be called animals.

⦿ Then let Us make living things that also have bodies but have no feelings or reasoning. Let Us make these grow from the Earth and let them produce everything that humans' and animals' bodies need. They will be called plants. So, animals and plants will be able to do some of the things humans

34

can do, similarly to the way people can do some of the things We can do. Let Us make all other living things to be unique and individual just like humans are, even those within the same group.

🔥 Yes – let every animal and plant and every place they live in be unique and individual.

🜂 Yet because people are My special gift for You, My Son, they will be different and superior to all other physical beings in their feeling, in their reasoning and in their behaviour. Let's make the knowledge of what We consider right and wrong be a part of them – their own unique characteristic – and let it be called their conscience.

🔥 Animals, plants and the world itself will be made for people, and to the world they will be the most special and the most important beings; just like people will be made for You, the Son and You will be the most important Person for them. Thus, let people be to animals and plants a reflection of what We will be to people: masters, carers and protectors.

Creativity

◈ Let's make people be in Our image in one other way – let them be creative like Us!

⍦ Great idea! Of course, just like We said when We discussed their ability to reproduce, unlike Us, people won't be able to make things out of nothing. But they will create from things that already exist – from things that We have made for them. In order for them to do that, let Us give them minds that will reflect Our mind.

♨ Indeed, let's make them able to create pictures, images and ideas in their minds and let that ability of theirs be called their imagination.

◈ Yes, let's make people able to dream, and wish, and imagine like Us. They will use their imagination to create things in their minds first and then they will use their bodies to mould and shape matter and make those images into physical objects in their world. They will also use their imagination to make non-physical creations in the world – expressions of their hearts and minds.

The Plan

◈ Images... Pictures... Reflections... That is how We will start but We will not stop there. We'll give them more. We'll make them more. We'll lift them higher... For the plan is bigger and better and fuller. I don't want to just give them to You, My Son,

🕇 I want to also give Myself to them, Father,

🔥 and I want You to do it through Me.

🜨 In this way they will not be only in Our image – a picture and reflection of Us – but they will be in Your likeness, My Son – in the likeness of God. In this way they won't just be able to *do* things like Us, but they will be able to *be* like Us. I will do it

🕇 in Me,

🔥 and through Me.

🜨 And so, I decided that after I had created them, I would one day begin to work within them, through them and with them to mould them into the likeness of the Son. In this way people would one day take part in Us...

🜨 We will share Our communion with them and they will dwell in Our glory. Like this they will become a part of Our fellowship and will join Us in Our never-ending relationship of love, unity and joy...

🕇 They will receive from Our love and share it amongst themselves and will give love back to Us. So We, God – Father, Son and Holy Spirit – will be in them and they will be in Us.

The Way

🜨 For people to come to share in Our glory, for humanity to come to take part in Our communion, I would first have to share in humanity – to take part in what makes people "people". So I said:

✹ My Son, would You go for Us and join people and take part in their humanity, sharing in what makes them people?

✟ It would be My greatest pleasure, Father.

🔥 It would be *My* greatest pleasure to help You in this.

✹ Like this through You, My Son, they will come to know Me.

✟ I will show them who You are, Father,

🔥 and it will all be done through Me.

🔯 Thus, after I'd made people in My image on the outside, I would go about making them in My likeness on the inside. It wouldn't happen from the beginning but eventually there would come a time when the Son would become one of them through the Holy Spirit and, like this, people would come to know the Father. So, in the end I, God – Father, Son and Holy Spirit – will be all and in all.

The Choice

🔯 There was just one last thing that had to be considered in My plan for people to one day come to be in My likeness. As part of being persons in My image meant that people would have freedom of choice, they would be free to choose to be with Me; to walk together with Me and work and partner together with Me in their path of growing in the knowledge of Us and Our ways, through which Our likeness will be fully formed in them. That is until they are joined and become one with Me like I – Father, Son and Holy Spirit – am One. They would also be free to choose to not be with Me, to not walk together with Me and to not partner with Me.

🜨 They would be free to go against all My desires, purposes and values and to live a life in opposition to everything that I am. If that happens, the process opposite to My desire and purpose for them will begin taking place within them.

⛨ Instead of growing in their knowledge of Me and adopting My likeness, they would break away from Our presence onto a path that will lead them to becoming more and more unlike Me in their thoughts, feelings, desires and behaviour.

🜂 The end of this process will be a complete, eternal and irreversible separation from Us in a place entirely devoid of the sense of and access to Our presence, Our influence and all that flows out from Us.

🜨 Let Us discuss how We would proceed should humanity reject Our purposes and choose instead the path of separation. Son, I know You're willing to become one of them if they choose to walk along the path that will lead them to Our likeness, but will You be willing to do it if they choose the path that leads away from Us?

⛨ Yes, Father, I am willing. I will become one of them either way so as to lift them up to My likeness, be it from their communion with Us or from their separation from Us... I will do it through My relationship with them and I will do what it takes for them to be able to come back to Us

🜂 with and through My help and mediation. As ever it will be My pleasure to do this.

🜨 Thus, should humanity choose to rebel against Our will for them, You will nonetheless make it possible for them to return to Us?

⛨ Yes, I will make a way back to Us and Our purposes for those people who want to return – only for those who turn away from their rebellion and accept walking on the path I will make for them.

🔥 And through You they will come to know the Father – the unknowable, the unsearchable, the One who dwells in inapproachable light – as He is revealed in You, the Son, through Me, the Holy Spirit.

🐦 That was how I, God, decided that I would meet humanity on either of the two paths they chose to walk on and invite them to that close communion with Me, which the Son would bring about. Thus, I would never abandon My plan of giving them an opportunity and granting them the ability to see My glory in and through the Son, no matter what circumstances they put themselves in.

The Witnesses

🌀 Son, this glorious process of becoming in Our likeness through their communion with Us will be so great, so magnificent... Why don't We enact it before others?

👑 Yes, let's make others be witnesses of it! Other beings – ones that will have a deeper and fuller understanding and insight into the greatness of this act than people will... They will be called angels – spiritual beings who exist to examine, study and be witnesses to humanity's ascent to the purposes We have for them.

🔥 Like humans, they will be persons and like humans, they will have a free will, yet unlike humans, they will not be creative nor will they be able to reproduce... They will exist to respond with worship to Us and Our actions, to observe and be in awe of Our dealings with humanity and to aid people in the path We have purposed for them with whatever means possible, as this will be pleasing to Us. So, angels will live and work towards making Our ultimate dream for humanity come to pass. They will be both My servants and servants of the humans We make – ministering spirits to those who would come to inherit the fullness of life in Us through the Son.

CHAPTER

Two
Dimensions

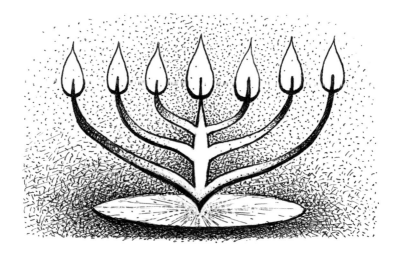

A Life-Changing Decision

⊕ Son, now that We've planned to create people and their world, let Us begin the process of creation itself. I Myself am ready to start.

⁜ I am ready too, Father, even though it means that it will no longer be just Us – Father, Son and Holy Spirit – but there will be other beings... Beings We'll have to accommodate and make provision for.

⁕ Our own existence will have to change so that Our creation's existence is made possible and so that it will be possible for them to relate to Us. We'll have to give up Our life by Ourselves and start sharing life with others.

⊕ They'll begin to partake in Our communion and in Our love and We'll begin to relate to and commune with them. It's a decision that will alter Our life as it is – a transition from Our life of sole existence. I am ready for this change.

⁜ So am I, Father.

⁕ I am too. Let Us begin.

Creation of Space and Time

⊕ Let there be a realm, a space, that will be aside and distinct from Us and Our existence. Let it be a place where Our creatures can experience life distinctly from Us in a dimension that is truly their own personal dwelling place.

⁜ Let this realm have two dimensions: a spiritual and

a physical one. Let the spiritual dimension exist forever and let the physical dimension be made temporal. That is, while the spiritual will never cease to be, the physical will be open to a process of change – a process that either brings about the end of its existence or its existence is extended and renewed.

🔥 Let the change the physical realm undergoes happen over time, a measurement that will be used to say how old something is – that is how long it has been in existence since its coming into the world. Let the spiritual realm be called the Heavens and the physical realm be called the Universe.

🜨 And so the two realms – the spiritual and the physical – were created.

God's Throne

🜨 Before We make anything else in the Heavens, let Us first make it a place where We manifest Ourselves – where We will reveal Our glory, power and splendour, Our majesty, perfection and holiness, Our unique nature and boundless wisdom.

🜨 Let Us dwell there in a position of government, a place from which We can rule over the whole of creation. Let Our position be a throne – a glorious throne in the highest heaven. Let the throne itself be a reflection of Us: let it reveal who We are and let it be a place where We make Ourselves visible to the whole of creation.

🔥 Let the throne be a place where the different angelic beings I will create will receive their orders and report to Us

on all matters relating to creation. Let it be a place where humans can approach Us through Me, the Holy Spirit, and which they can see with their spiritual senses in visions and dreams.

⊕ Let Us create four living beings around Our throne, and let them be spiritual beings who serve to reveal Our character and what We're like to the rest of creation. Let the living beings first and foremost reveal Our holiness – the fact that We are separate, different from everything We create and in a category of Our own.

⥁ Thus, let the living beings appear altogether other from all else that We create – let each have four faces and each have six wings. Let one of their faces represent Our kingly majesty so that those who see it might know that We are the King and supreme ruler over all creation. Let it have the face of one of the animals We will make that will symbolise these qualities on the Earth – an animal that will be considered kingly and majestic. Let this first face of the living beings be the face of a lion, the animal that will be associated with royal rule and kingly majesty.

⥁ Let their second face be another animal's face and let it represent Our boundless strength and Our unmatched endurance. Let it have the face of an ox – an animal that people will associate with power and perseverance.

⊕ Let their third face represent Our transcendence and Our undoubted superiority over all created things, and let that face also be of an animal that We'll create on the Earth. Let it be the face of an eagle – a bird that will rule the sky and symbolise supremacy and going beyond the known boundaries.

⥁ While the three faces of the living beings We've made

48

so far represent Our holiness and otherness from all that We create, let their fourth face represent Our approachability and the fact that We have decided to know and make Ourselves known to humanity in a way inaccessible to any other creature. Thus, let Us make the fourth face of the living beings to be a human face, which would communicate to creation that while I am entirely holy and inapproachable, Our deepest desire is to know humanity and for humanity to know Us in a true way.

🔥 Let this desire of Ours be shown also through making the living beings have human form and human hands under their wings to communicate that, to achieve Our desire for closeness with humankind one day You, the Son, will take human nature upon Yourself.

🕊 Yes, Holy Spirit, just like the living creatures symbolise, one day the Son will take up human nature. Through You, He will be able to stretch out a human hand towards the whole of humanity and lift them up to the position that We desire for them – to be not only in Our image but also in Our likeness. We, partakers in their humanity and they, partakers in Our love.

🕆 Let the four living beings be covered with eyes all over, which will represent Our omniscience. Then all will know that nothing in all of creation is ever hidden from Us. Let there also be four wheels around Our throne, one under each of the living beings, and let the wheels be directed by the living beings: let the wheels move up, down, left and right, whenever the living beings move.

🔥 Let this movement be a representation of Our omnipresence so that all of creation will know that We are everywhere and that no height, nor depth, nor length is hidden

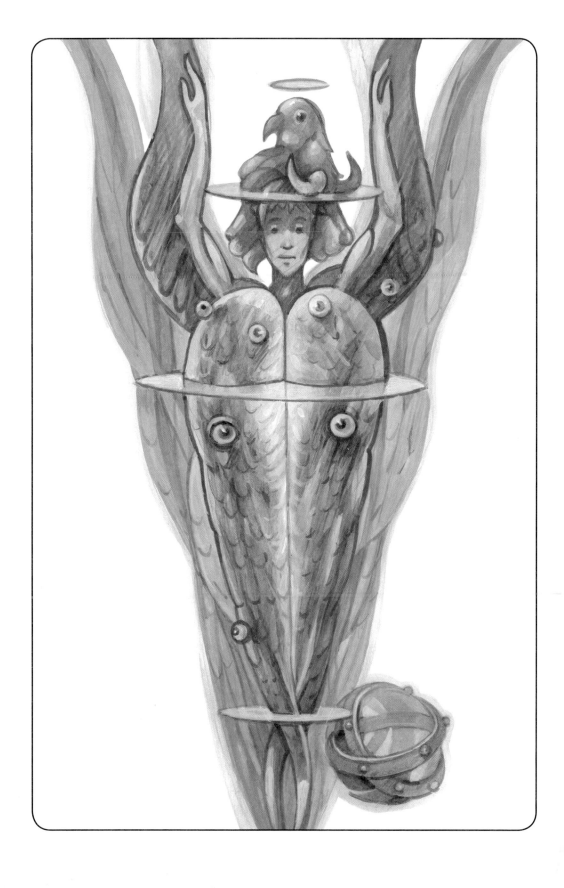

from Our presence. When the living beings stand before Us, let them, in response to what they see, say the word that best describes each of Us:

⊕ Holy,

⊤ Holy,

⊎ Holy.

⊕ And let them declare to all Our boundless might, Our eternal nature and Our transcendent glory.

⊛ At these words of Mine the living beings began to say:

> *Holy, holy, holy*
> *Is the Lord God Almighty*
> *Who was and is and is to come.*
> *Worthy, worthy, worthy*
> *Are You whose throne shines brightly –*
> *Glorious, may all Your will be done!*

⊕ Let Us make Our glory and transcendence visible in other ways, through symbols, colours, sounds and objects above, below and around the throne. Above the throne let Us create a brilliance – what will be seen as a collection of colours ordered in a certain way: first red, then orange, yellow, green, blue, indigo, violet.

⊤ Let this brilliance serve as a reminder that We, God the Father, God the Son and God the Holy Spirit, are the Creator of all things visible and invisible and that there is neither

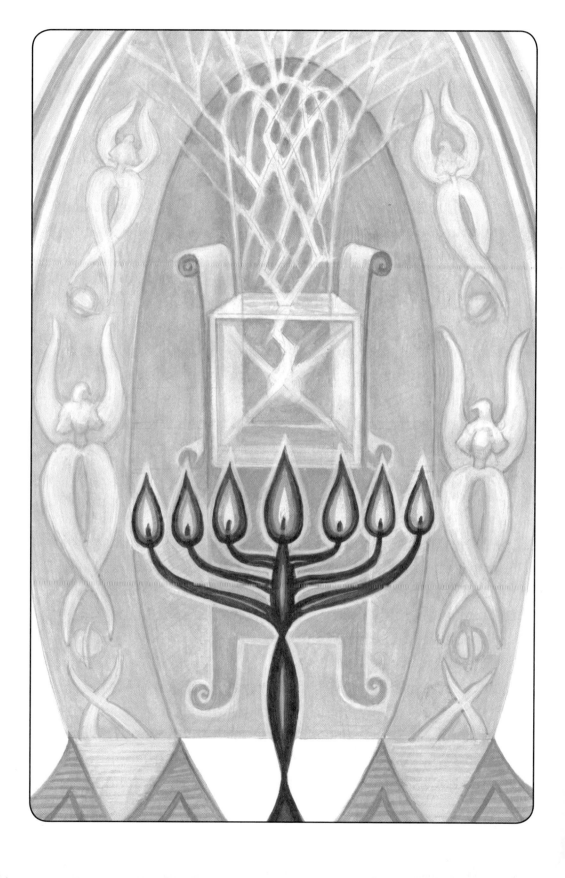

a pigment nor a colour combination in the whole Universe that didn't have its origin with Us.

🔥 Let there be an expanse under Our throne that will appear as a sea of glass, and let it be symbolic of Our complete supremacy over the elements – that Our power and authority are and will always be above and beyond all that We create. Let the transparency of the sea of glass represent the transparency, justice and truth which are the guiding principles of all Our rule over creation, so that all creatures will know that Our decisions are always true and always just because there is nothing hidden from Our sight.

🜨 Let the throne reveal Our inapproachability, Our complete and utter transcendence, Our incomprehensible and unknowable otherness, which no creature can fathom, nor draw near to, nor ever gain access to. Let that side of Ours be exuded from the centre of the throne through strong, flashing light and loud thundering.

🜋 Let Us also reveal Our desire to be known by Our creation – that in spite of Our inapproachability, We can be known through the revelation We give of Ourselves. Let the whole of creation know that We are a God who wants to be known and makes Himself known. Let this characteristic of Ours be manifested before Our throne so that all creation will know that, while We are inapproachable, You, Father, have chosen to reveal Yourself in Me, the Son, through You, the Holy Spirit.

🔥 Thus, let there be a visual representation of Me before Our throne – a lampstand with six branches and seven burning lamps of fire, which will communicate that even though We are One Spirit, We manifest Ourselves in different ways: as the Lord's Spirit, a spirit of wisdom and understanding, of counsel and strength, of knowledge and fear of the Lord.

⊗ Let the seven lamps illustrate that the Holy Spirit reveals different aspects of God – that He reveals Us as a loving and merciful God, as well as a holy and righteous One. A God who should be feared as well as loved, worshipped as well as praised.

Angelkind

⊗ Now, as We planned, let Us create the other beings that will inhabit the spiritual realm. Let Us make angelkind, which will be composed of the different kinds of angelic beings in the spiritual realm, who will also serve as a reflection of Us to the rest of creation and bring about Our purposes on the Earth.

⍦ Let one group of angelic beings be called seraphim and let them reveal Our holiness in Our dealings with the humans We will create. Like the four living beings, let the seraphim also declare Our might, but let them be focussed on revealing Our holiness and Our glory to the inhabitants of the Earth.

⍥ Let each seraph have six wings: two to fly with in readiness to do Our will and four to cover themselves with. This will show other creatures the reverence and awe they should have when approaching Our throne, always bearing in mind that We are a holy and awesome God.

⊗ Let there be another group of angelic beings called cherubim and let them reflect Our faithfulness, devotion and care for the whole of creation, and for humans in particular. Similar to the four living beings, let the cherubim also have four faces: let the first face be a cherub face, seen only on cherubim, and let it be representative of Our holiness – Our otherness and moral superiority to all creatures. Let the second face of the cherubim be a human face and let it represent Our desire for humans to draw near to Us; Our decision to be accessible and approachable to humanity. Let the third face be a lion face that will reveal Us as a sovereign ruler and King over all the works of Our hands. And let the fourth face of the cherubim be an eagle's face, again representative of Our transcendence and Our supremacy in power, knowledge and insight. Let the cherubim also have wings but let their wings be four: two to fly with and two to cover their bodies with.

꙼꙼ Let there be other beings in angelkind called simply "angels", who will be focussed on Our relationship with humanity and actively involved in bringing about Our purposes for the human race. Let the angels help humans understand Us better by serving to reveal Our character and Our will to humanity, and by encouraging people to live in a way that will make them able to reach Our desire for them: to ascend to the full wealth of the glorious knowledge of Us in Me and through the Holy Spirit.

꙼ After I made angelkind, I ordered them in a hierarchy and they were separated into different groups according to their strength, purpose and function. People won't know much about the angelic beings I made apart from those that play a special role in My story.

Three Special Angelic
Beings

⊕ Three angelic beings will be so important that We will make them known to people by their names. Let there be an archangel called Michael, one called Gabriel and a third, a cherub called Heylel. These beings are to have a special function in the world that We will create and in Our relationship with humanity. As they will be leaders of angels, they will also be known as "angels" themselves, even though they are beings higher in the angelic hierarchy.

⍦ Michael, Gabriel and Heylel will be in charge of the process by which We will achieve Our greatest plan for humanity. They will be overseers of the angels under them and make sure they know Our will and carry it out with precision.

♨ Michael will see and know Us in ways no one else does and thus will reflect this side of Us to people in ways only he can do. Gabriel will also be made to know aspects of Our being that no one else does in quite the same way and he too will reveal them to humanity. Similarly, the things that Heylel will be made to see in Us and will communicate to people will be special and specific to him.

Michael

🜔 Let the one who understands Our plans for humanity better than any other created being come forth now! He will be an angel of great strength and nobility and so will be called an archangel. Let him be someone who sees Our holiness with a clarity unusual for a being of his rank. Let the depth of his knowledge of Our uniqueness be comparable to the creatures closest to Us. Yet let that not move him from his position nor from his purpose, but let him be faithful to his task of overseeing humanity's ascent to Our glory.

🜔 Thus, let Us give him a name that reveals the special way in which he sees and understands Us – a name that reflects his character and his function... Let "Michael" mean "Who is like God?". Let the meaning of Michael's name not only speak about Our holiness and Our uniqueness, but let it be a name that reminds people how unfathomable and glorious We are, and what an unthinkable privilege it is for them to be invited to partake in Our communion.

🜔 Thus, every time people hear "Michael" – "Who is like God?" – let something within them say: "We are all invited to be so one day." If humanity chooses to walk away from Us and from the path that leads to Our purposes for them, then Michael will be the protector of those who choose Us and My ways. He will be the angel who will remind those people on the one hand that there is no one like God – that there is no one worthier of their attention, love and praise – and on the other that the invitation to the abundance of My glory is still valid – that We are a God who keeps His promises and works His purposes in the lives of those who seek Us.

Gabriel

⊗ Let Michael not be the only being We make whose name reveals the nature and purpose for which We created him. In fact, let Us create things in this way in general. Let Us give them names that will reflect their character.

⯑ This is an excellent idea! Let Us make an angel who sees Our power in a special way and whose name will mean "God is strong". If it so happens that people choose to walk away from Us, let Gabriel be the angel whose name will remind those who choose Us that Our power is without limit. Let "Gabriel" – "God is strong" – remind people that We are powerful enough to keep Our promises, to fulfil Our word and achieve Our purposes.

⯑ Thus, if humanity chooses the path that leads them away from Us, Gabriel will be the one who will communicate to people who seek Us those plans and purposes of Ours which would seem impossible to them, and which could only come to pass if My power is manifested on the Earth. Let Gabriel be the angel who understands better than anyone how important it is for people to know Our plans and purposes, to understand My instructions and to follow Our leading.

Heylel

⊗ Let the third angel, the cherub, be someone who understands, like no other created being does, My desire to re-

veal Myself to people through the Son and for them to come to be in His likeness. Let him understand like no one else that the key to people rising to this glorious purpose of Ours is in them knowing Us personally.

⚜ The degree to which they come to know Us personally is the degree to which they will attain to Our likeness. Thus, let this angel's name mean "light-bearer" and "light-bringer", as he will himself possess light revealing the knowledge of God and will carry this knowledge to the people We make. Heylel will be the angel responsible for helping people gain a deeper knowledge of Our Being. He will show them what We're like and what's foreign to Our nature – Our beauty and splendour, Our preferences, Our desires and the way in which We want the world to develop.

⚜ Let Heylel see and understand the steps humans need to take in order to come to share in the fullness of Our communion – let him see their needs, what they still lack and what they need help with, and let him be the one who will seek specific guidance from Us as to how best to help humanity in this process.

⚜ As Heylel will be the angel who will see and know Us in ways no other created being does, let Us create something he will use to express what he sees in Us in a special way. It will not be a physical creation but it will manifest itself in the physical realm as sounds... groups and collections of sounds... melodies... symphonies... Music!

⚜ Indeed, let Heylel be a musician, the leader of the heavenly choir that sings about and glorifies Us to the whole of creation. And let him understand a truth and so teach humanity: that their worship of God will help them gain that knowledge of Us – that greater, deeper, more intimate

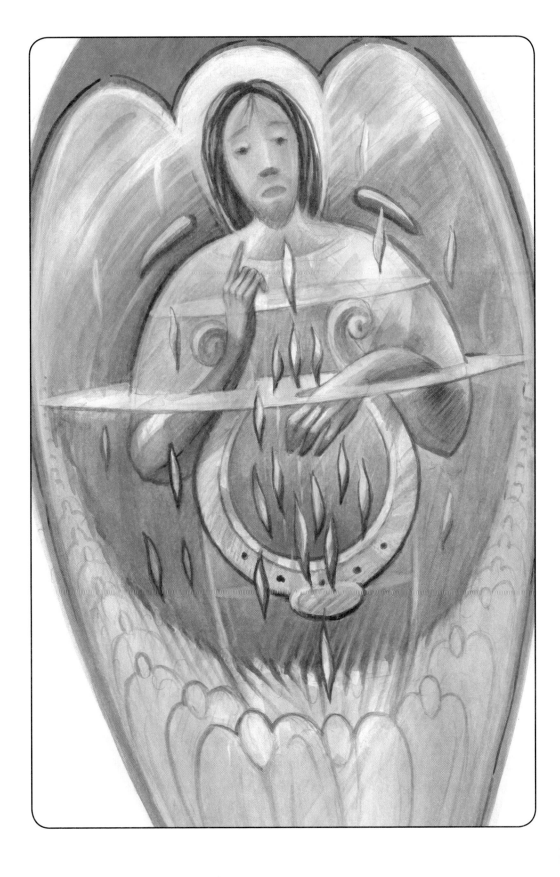

knowledge, which leads them along the path to the fullness of life in and with Us.

☯ Thus Heylel was the first person to ever receive the gift of music and with it, he gained an understanding about the power of worship. Here is the first song he sang after he was created:

Maker of the Universe,
Wonderful and True
God of Highest Heaven,
Who compares to You?

You are glorious my King
And worthy of all praise
Show me more and I will sing
About You all my days.

With the making of Michael, Gabriel and Heylel, I completed My creation of the spiritual beings. These three angels were to be the most important angels in aiding people to inherit the glory that I had prepared for them.

The Universe and the Galaxies

◉ Now let Us begin setting up the physical dimension. Let there be two types of entities, which will be known as heavenly bodies, in the Universe: let the first type be collections of burning gases that give out their own heat and their

own light, and let the second type be collections of solid matter that do not give out their own heat nor their own light, but that reflect the light of the first type of entities.

♈ Now let both types of entities be set in motion – a distancing from one another, which will cause them to be shaped and grouped together, and let each group contain both types of heavenly bodies. Let the groups be called galaxies and let each galaxy contain both types of heavenly bodies – light-emitting and light-reflecting ones.

♨ Let the position and movement of the individual entities and their galaxies be set and governed by rules, which people will call physical laws, and which will be the foundational principles behind their individual existences as well as their interactions with the rest of the physical world.

CHAPTER

CREATING THE EARTH

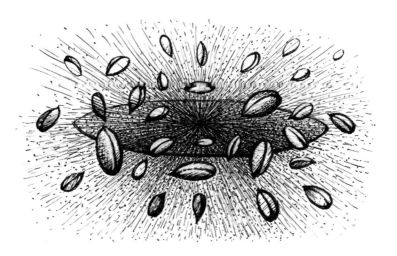

Setting Up the Planet

🜂 Now it is time to begin Our work on the place that will sustain life and be a home for people and for the other living things that will exist alongside them. Let Us take one of the galaxies We've created and let Us set it up in such a way that there will be a place in it that will be a home for the people We planned to create. Son, over there is the biggest galaxy We've made, but let Us not take that one.

🜊 Yes, Father, and neither let Us take this one over here – the most beautiful galaxy We've made. Rather, let Us take *this* galaxy – this small one over here.

🜋 Yes, let Us take that one – the one that is neither the biggest nor the most beautiful of the galaxies We've made. And let this choice of Ours communicate to the spiritual beings We have created, and to the physical beings We will create, that neither size nor beauty add value to things We create, but rather what matters is Our interaction with them.

🜂 Let it show that I, God, am the One who is able to take the smallest and most insignificant things in all creation and relate with them in such a way that they become the focus of My attention and of My affection; so that the things that are small are made to reflect My greatness, the things that are bland are made to reflect My beauty and the insignificant things are made to reflect My glory.

🜊 Let the larger heavenly bodies that are collections of matter in the galaxy, which do not give out their own heat or light, be called planets and let them be of various sizes. Let the smaller ones of them be called moons – bodies that are at a set distance away from the planets and that revolve around the planets.

🔥 Let the heavenly bodies that are collections of gases giving out their own heat and light be called stars and let them be of various sizes.

🜨 Let Us now choose a planet from this galaxy – this smaller one over here – and let Us make it the only planet in the galaxy to contain all the physical elements necessary for life to exist. Let Us set it up as a home for the people We will make – it shall be called the Earth.

⚲ Let Us now mould and shape the Earth and let Us put it in order by joining its elements in such a way as to make it possible for plant and animal life to spring up from it.

🔥 Yet let Us do Our work on the Earth, acting not only from a distance but let Us also be near it – let *Me* hover over it!

🕊 The moment the Holy Spirit said this, the angels who had already gathered round to watch Me begin My work on the Earth gasped in astonishment. It was then that Michael, Gabriel and Heylel stood in the midst of the angels and began speaking to them:

🜎 To all of you gathered round, let us explain why the Almighty, the One who sustains all of creation, the One who is the Source of all life, has decided to not only create the Earth but to be in the closest possible proximity while He forms and shapes it. The Lord has decided to make the Earth a suitable home for creatures He plans to make – creatures He will call people and whom He will make in His own image and likeness.

🕊 The angels echoed the words in bewilderment:

"IN HIS OWN IMAGE AND LIKENESS!"

70

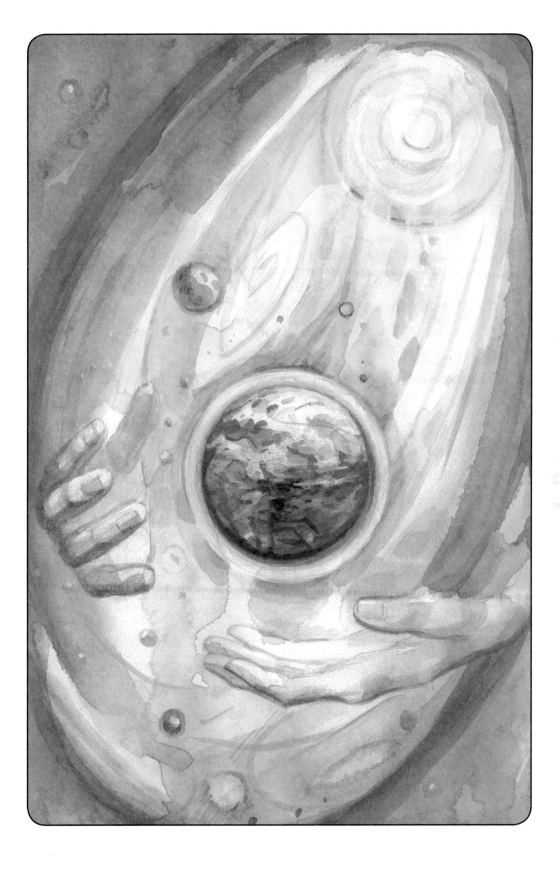

The heavenly beings would never have thought it possible that I, the Maker of all things, both visible and invisible, would ever move from My throne and Myself draw so near to something I'd created. Michael continued:

🕊 The Lord has not only chosen to grace us with the privilege of witnessing His creative work on the Earth, but He has also decided that we, the angels, will aid humanity in attaining to all that God has prepared for them. He has appointed the three of us – me, Michael, and Gabriel and Heylel – to be overseers of all the angels' work in this process.

🕊 The Almighty has revealed to the three of us His plans for humanity and He has instructed us how to lead all of you in your mission.

🕊 So now you are all to observe God's creative work on the Earth with the utmost care, doing your very best to grasp, from the things He does, how important humans are to Him and how strongly He desires them to enter into the bounty of communion with Him and experience His glory.

🕊 The angels listened intently to Heylel's instruction and, while he was speaking, the air of astonishment and excitement in their ranks began to slowly be replaced by an atmosphere of confidence and determination. You see, there is nothing more important or more pleasing to the angels than to do My will and to see My purposes being accomplished. Having found out that they also had a part to play in My plans for humanity, the angels quickly set aside their excitement and directed their energy to the mission at hand. They turned their attention towards the Earth and saw that it was still formless and void, and that darkness was over the surface of the deep. It was then that the Holy Spirit descended upon the Earth and began hovering over the surface of the waters.

Then I said:

🜂 Let there be light!

🜂 And light appeared. When I saw it, I said:

🜂 The light is good, Father! So let Us separate the light from the darkness. The light shall be called "day" and let the darkness be called "night".

🜂 And so it happened. There was evening and there was morning – the Earth's very first day. Then I said:

🜂 Let there be an expanse in the midst of the waters and let it separate the waters from the waters.

🜂 And so it happened – I separated the waters below the expanse from the waters above the expanse. I then said:

🜂 Let the expanse be called "sky".

🜂 Again, there was evening and there was morning, the Earth's second day. I then said:

🜂 Let the waters on the surface of the Earth be gathered into one place and let the dry land appear. Let the dry land be called "earth" and let the waters that are gathered together be called "seas".

🜂 It is good!

🜂 Now that We've separated the waters from the dry land, let Us create the first living organisms – plants. Let the plants sprout from the Earth: vegetation, plants yielding seed and fruit trees bearing fruit after their kind with seed in them. Let the plants' ability to bear fruit after their kind be contained within their seeds. Let every seed contain all the information necessary for a new plant to grow from it under the right conditions that the Earth provides. Let this model of seeds carrying information for the making of new organisms apply to all living things We will create from now on.

🜂 And so it happened. The Earth brought forth vegetation, plants yielding seed after their kind and trees bearing fruit with seed in them, after their kind. I again looked at what I had made and saw that it was also good. And there came evening and there came morning – the Earth's third day. Then I continued:

⚕ Now let Us arrange the biggest star in the Earth's galaxy in the sky to govern the day, separating the light from the darkness, and to give light on the Earth. Let this star be called the Sun and let it stay at just the right distance from the Earth to provide the right amount of light and warmth for life to be sustained on the planet.

♨ Let the Earth have one Moon and let this Moon be in the sky to govern the night, separating the darkness from the light, and to reflect the Sun's light on the Earth during the night. Let the Sun and the Moon serve as signs on the Earth to mark time, separating it into days, months, seasons and years.

⊛ Now let the other stars in the Earth's galaxy be made visible in the sky, and let them be ordered in such a way as to form patterns that people will name after their ideas about the physical and spiritual world. Let these patterns be called constellations and let them serve as signposts for people's movement on the Earth.

⊛ And so it happened. I set up the Sun, the Moon and the stars in the sky and I saw that that too was good. There again came evening and morning – the fourth day. Then I said:

⊛ Son, it is now time for Us to create the animals that will inhabit the Earth.

⚕ Yes, Father, let them be of two kinds – animals with backbones that will be known as vertebrates and animals without backbones that will be known as invertebrates. Let

74

Us make five groups of vertebrates: amphibians that will live both on land and in water, reptiles that will live on land but will also go into water, birds that will live on land but can fly in the air, fish that will live underwater and mammals, some of which will live on land and some in water.

🖐 Let amphibians, reptiles and fish be cold-blooded and let birds and mammals be warm-blooded. Let amphibians, reptiles, fish and birds lay eggs from which their young ones will hatch. Let mammals give birth to their young ones and let their bodies produce milk to feed their young ones after birth. Now let the waters teem with swarms of living creatures: vertebrates and invertebrates, amphibians, mammals and fish. Let there be birds that fly above the Earth in the open expanse of the sky!

🕉 I saw that it was good and spoke to the animals I'd made:

🕉 I bless you this day: be fruitful and multiply! Sea creatures, fill the waters and the seas! Birds, multiply on the Earth!

🕉 And there was evening and there was morning – that was the fifth day. Then I said:

🕉 Let the Earth bring forth creatures after their kind: vertebrates and invertebrates, reptiles and mammals.

🕉 Thus, I made every creature that moves on the ground after its kind and I saw that it was good. Then I said:

🕉 Now that We have made plants and animals and have arranged the Sun in the sky, let Us create a relationship between these living things and the Sun, which will sustain all physical life on the planet. Let plants produce food for animals and people – let their leaves, seeds and fruit contain all the nutrients necessary for their bodies.

⚕ Let plants also produce their own food by taking in light from the Sun, water from the soil and a gas that people will call carbon dioxide. While making their own food, let them also produce oxygen – a gas that animals and people will breathe in from the air on Earth.

⚘ When breathing, let animals and plants breathe out carbon dioxide – the gas that plants need to take in. Let this relationship between the Sun, plants and animals – the balance, harmony and mutual dependence in which they exist – be a reflection of Our own life together in harmony as Father, Son and Holy Spirit.

⚭ Let it serve to reveal to the rest of creation that everything We make is perfect; that We create all things with a purpose; that We have set up all things in creation to be mutually dependent on one another so that all creatures affect all others, no matter how small and insignificant some may appear.

Creating People

⚗ Now that I had made the Earth, having set the Sun, Moon and stars in their places and created the plants and animals, it was time to create those for whom I had made all this: the most important creation of all – people.

⚭ Son, We have made the Earth a suitable home for people. We can now begin creating them – the gift of love that I, the Father have chosen to give to You, My Son.

⚕ It is time.

🔥 Let the dust of the ground rise up! Let it take the shape of a figure standing upright on two legs.

☸ At this the angels, who had until now calmly been observing My creative work on the Earth, suddenly became restless as they hadn't seen Me make any other upright creature. Seeing their reaction, Michael, Gabriel and Heylel spoke to them:

⛎ The Lord is making humans upright in order to distinguish them from the animals He has made. While people are going to be similar to the animals in many ways, God will make them to be in a category of their own because they are going to rule over the Earth and over all living things on the Earth.

⛎ Man is going to be ruler over the Earth similar to the way the Lord rules over heaven.

⛎ Indeed, the Lord will make Man to be like a god to the rest of the creatures on the Earth. He is going to have abilities that no other creature on the Earth has. He is going to have a relationship with God like no other creature on Earth and will come to have a relationship with Him like no creature in heaven.

☸ When the angels heard this explanation, they regained their composure somewhat, although this new revelation of Man being like a god to the rest of the Earth's creatures came as a shock to most of them. I continued My work on Man with the words:

🜨 As We decided that there would be both a physical and a non-physical part to Man, let Us now make Man's brain to be the organ where their thoughts, will and emotions will be formed. Let them sense the expressions of their inner being in the area of their heart and stomach and let them show these expressions through their face and gestures.

♈ Yes, let their mind, will, emotions and their ability to communicate using speech and language be controlled by different parts of the brain. Let Man use his face to make his emotions visible to others. Let him use his mouth to speak and to communicate his thoughts and let his voice express the depth of his emotions.

☖ Let Man use his hands to take care of his body, to care for the Earth and for other living things, and to create new things. As We planned, let Man use his physical senses to interact with the physical world and his spiritual senses to interact with the spiritual world. Let this first human being be made male – a man who will later be joined to a female for them to form a family and have children together, just as We planned.

☸ And so it happened – the first human being I made was male. I made Man upright and his brain more capable than the brains of animals. I gave him hands, which he would be able to use for various purposes, and senses with which to interact with the physical and the spiritual world. It was now time to make him distinguishable from the animals in one more aspect – the most important of all:

☖ As Man is the only creature destined to live in Our fellowship, let Us give him something from Us – something that no other earthly creature has. Let this be the ultimate distinction between Man and the other earthly creatures, which shows to all created beings, both in the Heavens and on the Earth, that Man is the most important of all Our creatures; that We have made him to be master over the Earth, to rule over all earthly creatures and to be a carrier of Our glory!

꙳ Let Man emanate Our glory – let his body be surrounded with the substance, with the brilliance from around Our throne that reveals to creation Our power, Our magnificence and Our boundless worth.

꙳ And so I took some of My glory and placed it upon Man. The angels' astonishment was so great at this that they did not utter a sound. You see, My glory is so unfathomable and so beyond the reach of created beings, that it would be unthinkable for a creature to ever touch My glory, let alone carry it upon themselves. Then I continued:

꙳ Now that Man's body is complete, We can make him a living being by breathing the breath of life into him. Yet before We do this, let Us appear on the Earth in a form that will make it easier for Man to communicate with Us. One day We will reveal Ourselves to Man as Father, Son and Holy Spirit, but for now let him see Our unity in a body like his own.

꙳ Let Us make the angels also appear to people on the Earth in human form, and let them communicate with people using human language in their mission to help people become what We have called them to be.

꙳ And so it happened, to the angels' greatest astonishment and wonder yet. I appeared on the Earth in a form similar to Man's, and when angels were to later appear to Man, Man would see them and communicate with them as with people. Then I said:

꙳ Now let Man be made a living being – let the breath of life enter him!

꙳ At these words of Mine, Man took his very first breath. He then opened his eyes and looked at Me – the moment I had been longing for ever since I first thought about creating him. I said to him:

☯ Hello! I am the Lord God. I am the One who created you. You are Man and you shall be called Adam.

☯ Adam looked at Me and then began to examine himself. He stretched out his arms and his legs and looked at his hands and feet. He touched his head, ran his fingers through his hair and touched his ears, then his chin and then his face. He scrunched up his nose, raised his eyebrows, opened and closed his mouth several times and touched his tongue with the tip of his index finger. Then he took a deep breath and said his first words:

⚭ God... You... You made me?

☯ Yes. I created you.

☯ Adam repeated the sentence to himself, taking in every word. Then, looking at the angels that were all around us, he asked:

⚭ And who are they?

☯ They are angels, Adam – beings that I created to serve Me and to help you in your life.

☯ Adam looked at them again, this time with more understanding. The angels responded by gathering closer to him, both in amazement and curiosity, thinking to themselves, "So *this* is the creature chosen to ascend to God's likeness..." Studying their appearance, Adam said:

⚭ Angels... Hello, angels!

☯ They all said hello to him, the most confident of course being Michael, Gabriel and Heylel, who introduced themselves to him by name.

⚭ Hello, Adam, I'm Michael. I'm glad to finally meet you. I am an archangel, one of the three chief angels responsible for overseeing the other angels' work and interaction with you. My name means "Who is like God?" and I am devoted to serve as a reminder of God's uniqueness, holiness and of His ultimate plan and purpose for humanity.

👼 Hi, I'm Gabriel. My name means "God is strong" and I'm devoted to serve as a reminder of God's power and faithfulness to fulfil His promises and to achieve His purposes. I've been waiting for this moment for a while now.

👼 So have I. My name is Heylel, which means "light-bearer" and "light-bringer", and I am devoted to bringing the light of the knowledge of God to humanity. I look forward to seeing how your life will unfold.

🐍 Adam didn't quite know what to make of these greetings but accepted them and then, turning towards Me, asked:

👤 And now?

🐍 Now you and I will be together, Adam – living, walking, communing.

👤 Living, walking, communing... where?

🐍 I will make a special place for us here on the Earth: a garden where you will live and where I will come to meet with you.

🐍 So Adam stood by and watched Me create his home:

🐍 Let there be a garden towards the East, over there, in that place that will be called Eden. Let the Garden of Eden be a place of beauty like no other place on the Earth. Let there be all kinds of plants there – flowers, shrubs and trees – that are pleasing to the sight and good for food. Let there also be a river that flows out of Eden to water the garden and let it divide from there, becoming four rivers.

🐍 People would later call the first of the four rivers Pishon and it would flow around the whole land of Havilah, where there is gold, bdellium and the onyx stone. The second river they would call Gihon, which would flow around the whole land of Cush. The third river they would call Tigris, which would flow east of Assyria, and the fourth river they would call the Euphrates. When Adam saw the garden I had created for him, he exclaimed:

𓀭 So many colours, sounds and fragrances! Such beauty! And *this* place... this... *paradise*, will be my home?!

𓀭 Yes, Adam, this is where you will live. But it is not yet complete.

𓀭 It's not? But, God, what more could you make for me? This place is *perfect*!

𓀭 I am still to make two more trees, Adam – the most important trees in the Garden of Eden. Without these trees in the garden our life together would be impossible.

𓀭 Puzzled at My words, Adam took a step back while I spoke:

𓀭 Let the Tree of Life and the Tree of the Knowledge of Good and Evil be planted over here in the middle of the garden and let them bear fruit.

𓀭 So, the two special trees were planted and My work on the Garden of Eden was now complete. I took Adam, led him into Eden and said to him:

𓀭 Your home is now ready for you, Adam. You can begin your life here – life together with Me. You are to cultivate and keep the garden.

From any tree of the garden you may eat freely; but from the Tree of the Knowledge of Good and Evil you shall not eat, for on the day that you eat from it you will surely die.

𓀭 Adam repeated My commands under his breath, thinking carefully about every word. Of course, he didn't know what "to die" meant and, judging from the angels' reactions, he could see that he wasn't alone in this. When the angels heard My warning to Adam, they began repeating the new word questioningly, turning around and looking for someone to explain it to them. Then Heylel said in a loud voice for all to hear:

᠅ We do not know what "dying" is either, but we believe that when the time is right the Lord will make it clear to us.

᠅ At this the angels calmed down. Then I said to Myself, "It is not good for Adam to be alone. I will make for Him a suitable helper..."

᠅ Adam, you need a companion, a helper suitable for you – someone you can live with, work with and have children with.

᠅ Where can I find such a creature?

᠅ I will bring all the beasts of the field and every bird of the sky before you for you to name them and to choose a helper for yourself from among them.

᠅ So I brought all the animals I had made to Adam. And after he had given names to all of them, he said to Me:

᠅ I have completed my task. I named all the animals and found several helpers from among the hoofed animals to aid me with various tasks in the garden. I also found that some animals enjoy my company more than others – it is those that I can see myself building friendship with. However, I did not find the kind of helper and companion You described, God.

᠅ Why is that, Adam?

᠅ When I began naming them, the animals obeyed my every word. But not a single one of them showed itself capable of helping me with all my tasks, nor was any one able to communicate the same kinds of thoughts and ideas as I can. Through my interaction with them I could see that You have made me... different... superior to them... similar to the way

You are superior to me.

🜨 You have judged correctly, Adam. I *have* made you different and superior to the animals; I have made you to be their master similar to the way I am your Master. Cultivating and keeping the garden is your task, your work here on the Earth. You need someone able to help you with this and also to have the same capacities and intellect as you. You need someone of your own kind, who will live and work alongside you, not as your inferior but as someone whose strengths and giftings complement yours. Together you will also rule over the animals.

👤 Lord, where can I find such a person? The angels are also not suitable for me.

🜨 I will create one for you, Adam, as you now know, like I do, exactly what you need.

🜨 So I caused a deep sleep to fall upon Adam. Then I took one of his ribs and closed up the flesh at that place. I said:

🜨 Let Adam's rib be fashioned into a Woman – a female human being who will be a suitable helper and companion for him. Let her be able to conceive and bear Adam's children in her body, and feed them after they're born the way mammals are made to do. Let Woman's body be slightly smaller than Adam's – let her bones be smaller and lighter and let her be physically weaker than Man. Let her also be a carrier of Our glory and let her come alive!

🜨 At My words the Woman became a living being. I introduced Myself to her the way I did to Adam and I showed her the Garden of Eden. I then brought her to Adam and when he woke up, he saw her and said with astonishment, joy and understanding:

ꙮ This is now bone of my bones, and flesh of my flesh – a helper and companion suitable for me. She shall be called Woman, because she was taken out of Man.

ꙮ I turned to both of them:

ꙮ I bless you now – be fruitful and multiply; fill the Earth and subdue it; rule over the fish of the sea and over the birds of the sky and over every living thing that moves on the Earth.

You may eat every plant yielding seed that is on the surface of all the Earth, and from every tree which has fruit yielding seed.

To every beast of the Earth and every bird of the sky and to everything that moves on the Earth which has life, I have also given every green plant for food.

Be together forever! Share life, joys and challenges! Find joy in each other and all you do together. Trust, support and help each other and grow to the fullness of My purpose for your lives!

ꙮ When Adam heard this, he held out his hands and embraced his wife. Seeing this, all other creatures that were gathered around – angels and animals – began to rejoice and celebrate the Man and the Woman's union. After the cheering quietened down, I continued:

ꙮ As you can both see, you are different from one another – Adam is a man – male – and you, his wife, are a woman – female. Both of you – Man and Woman, male and female – are made in My image. For this reason, a man shall leave his father and his mother and be joined to his wife and they shall become one flesh.

ꙮ Then Adam spoke to his wife:

ꙮ Your name will be Eve, which means "living", because

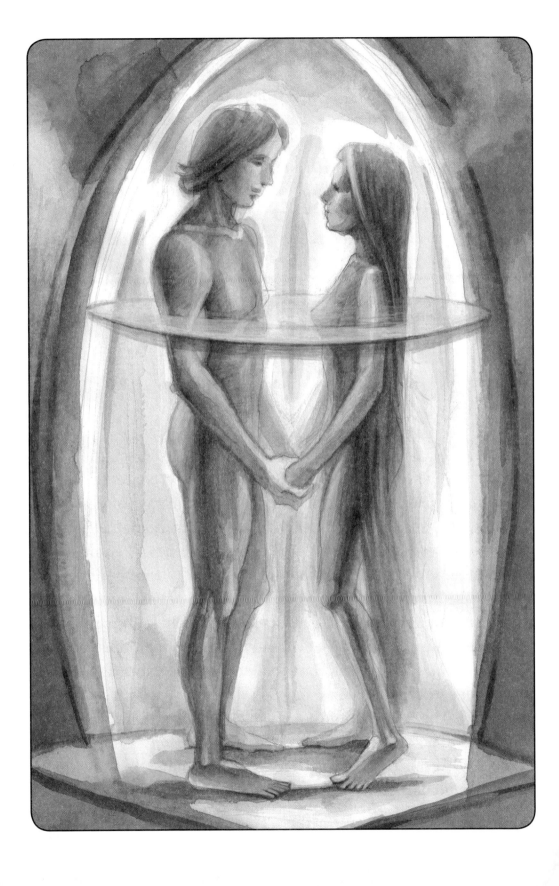

you will be the mother of all the living.

   ⊗ And so it happened – Adam and Eve now knew they were husband and wife, created in Our image and given the task to have children and to rule over the Earth and over all living things. They were both naked, yet they were not ashamed, as shame and other bad things hadn't yet entered the world. They were carriers of My glory and that made their perception of Me, themselves and one another clear, right and complete.

The Seventh Day

Celebration

   ⊗ Adam and Eve began their life in perfect contentment, a life of pleasure and not lacking anything in the Garden of Eden, whose very name means "delight". The human couple were the very last beings I created, as all things I had made before them – both spiritual and physical – were designed to make human existence possible, and for people to be able to have a relationship with Me and eventually ascend to My likeness. As all life was now ready to grow, reproduce and develop by itself, it was time for Me to mark the end of My creative work in a special way. So I declared:

   ⊗ The heavens, the Earth and all beings that dwell in them are now complete!

   ⊗ At this the angels began to rejoice, filling the air with the sound of their voices. I continued:

☯ I therefore bless this day, the seventh day, and I declare it to be a holy day – a day set apart from all the previous days. It will be a day on which I will not work as I have done in the past six days, but I will celebrate with all My creatures the completion of My creation.

☯ The angels' voices rose up again and this time when the earthly creatures heard their rejoicing, they joined in and each in their own way expressed their joy at My words. Then Heylel said:

😇 My Lord, if You permit, I will sing a song in celebration of this holy day.

☯ Seeing My approval, Heylel began his song:

Before time began
The Lord stretched forth the heavens –
Give Him praise!
He laid out the Earth,
And made it home for people
In just six days.

Then the Lord declared
"The seventh day have I prepared
To be a holy celebration
That marks the end of My creation!"

How great it is
The life that God has given us –
Praise His name!
This act of His:
His kindness, goodness, care,
Let all proclaim!

Heylel's voice carried throughout creation and every creature heard the lyrics to his song. Seeing their desire to join in with the singing, Heylel turned to the angels, Adam and Eve and the animals, who had already gathered around him in expectation, and proclaimed:

🕉 This is how we will sing it: each of us will sing a different part of the song and some parts we will all sing together. Are you ready?

☯ At this, Heylel taught his song to the angels and to Adam and Eve. Some of the animals endowed with musical skills also joined in, adding their personal touches to the melody and rhythm. When they were ready, they all presented themselves before Me and sang Heylel's song in My presence, with each creature taking part. That is how My creatures spent the seventh day – singing and celebrating the end of My creation. They rejoiced together at the life I had given them to share in My presence, in the world I had created for them, and were excited about getting to know Me and one another.

Adam and Eve could now begin their life in communion with Me and with the angels, as masters and protectors over the Earth and its creatures.

CHAPTER

GUARDIANS OF
THE EARTH

Before Meeting with
Adam and Eve

🜂 After the Sun had set on the seventh day celebrations and Eve and her husband Adam had fallen asleep in their home, the Garden of Eden, I announced with joy:

🜃 Son, the time has finally come for Us to begin Our communion with Adam and Eve!

🜔 Yes, Father, tomorrow We will begin teaching them about Us: about who We are and the kind of God We are.

🜍 We will also teach them about themselves; about how they can best fulfil their task of ruling over the Earth; about Our ultimate purpose for them to gain a deeper knowledge of who We are and to enter the richness of Our fellowship.

🜂 I then summoned the three chief angels and said to them:

🜂 Michael, Gabriel and Heylel, tomorrow We will begin teaching Adam and Eve about the life We have given them. You are to gather round Us and listen carefully so that you will be prepared to pass on what We teach them to the other angels. Remember, We made people in Our image and your task is to help them on their journey to gain the fullness of what We have prepared for them.

🜨 Yes, Lord, we will do our very best.

🜨 To serve You and the people You have made will be our utmost priority.

🜨 We will devote ourselves fully to the task you have given us, Lord.

95

Daily Meeting

⊛ The following morning I entered the Garden of Eden just as Adam and Eve were waking up, and greeted them:

⊛ Good morning, Adam! Good morning, Eve! Did you sleep well?

ᚷᚹ I did, thank you.

ᚠᚹ So did I, thank you.

ᚷᚹ After sleeping we feel so... refreshed.

⊛ I made your bodies in this way. During sleep your body regains its strength and your mind has time to process the information it has received from the outside world.

ᚠᚹ Our mind is what we think with?

⊛ That's right, Eve.

ᚷᚹ Ah, so we think, want and feel with our inner being... We also seem able to sense Your and the angels' presence in the garden, even before we hear or see You.

⊛ Yes, I have also designed your hearts in such a way that you are able to sense and interact with the spirit world.

ᚠᚹ So, You and the angels are spirits?

⊛ Yes, the angels and I are spiritual but we manifest ourselves to you in bodies that will be visible to your physical eyes. The angels will usually appear to you in human form. The ones you see here with us are Michael, Gabriel and Heylel. They will be joining our company, listening to our conversations so that they will be able to pass on to the other angels the things I teach you. The angels' job is to aid you in your life – they will help you better understand and put into practice the things you learn from Me.

⊛ Adam and Eve, who had been focussed solely on Me and our conversation, now acknowledged the angels' presence with us. They looked at Michael, Gabriel and Heylel, nodded in appreciation and then turned their attention back to Me. Adam said:

◊ So we, humans, have a physical and a non-physical side?

⊛ Yes, and they are connected. The inner being cannot live without the body and the body cannot exist without the life within. Your body is the carrier of your spirit and it makes your interaction with the physical world possible.

◊ So only physical beings can naturally act on the physical world?

⊛ That's right. As you remember, yesterday, on the Earth's seventh day, we celebrated the end of My creation. I made the Earth to be your home and I made you masters over it and over all living things. What kind of masters would you be if I or someone else could act here, independently of you?

◊ So, You and the angels could act here if we wanted you to?

⊛ At this, I signalled to Michael to respond to her and he said:

⚕ The Lord has made you and your husband to have authority over the Earth and all life on it. Therefore, you and the animals left in your charge are the only ones who can act here. We can, however, assist you in your decision-making and help you in your life here if you want us to. In this sense, we cannot act on the Earth, but we can influence the things that happen here when people need our help.

⊛ Hearing this, they both turned to Me in astonishment:

👥 So God, You made *us* rule over the Earth the way You rule over the heavens?

🜨 That's right, My precious one.

👥 That is so... generous of You... so kind...

👥 Thank You, God, for doing this for us. You could have created us in a different way but instead You gave us this life, this... freedom!

🜨 Adam, life in communion with you and with Eve was what I dreamed of. I wanted our relationship to be based on love, and love requires freedom. I have made you free to choose how you will live your life on the Earth. You are the ones who will choose the extent to which I and the angels will have an impact on your lives.

👥 God, we want You to be involved in our life, to teach us and to guide us.

👥 We want to meet with You every day.

🜨 Very well. I would like that very much. Why don't you meet Me here every evening, at the end of each day? At those times we could discuss your experiences, go over any questions you may have and any plans and desires that may arise in your hearts during the day.

👥 Great!

👥 Perfect!

🜨 You will know the time for our meeting has come when you sense a calling, an invitation inside you...

👥 In our hearts?

🜨 That's right. It will come like a wind blowing through your being, summoning you to our meeting place.

👥 Thank you, God. So... we'll see You tonight.

🜨 Yes, Eve. I'll see you both tonight. Enjoy your first day together as masters over the Earth!

With these words, I walked away from Adam and Eve, and the angels also distanced themselves, leaving My precious people to go and experience for themselves the world I had created for them. Seeing that they were now alone, Adam said to Eve:

👤 Let's take a walk and explore this beautiful garden that the Lord has given to us, Eve.

👤 Yes, and let's go and see the animals too!

Exploring the Earth

☙ And off they went through the garden, rejoicing to be in one another's company and delighting in the beauty of their paradise home. They bathed under the waterfalls, swam in the streams, smelled the different flowers and tasted the different kinds of fruit that grew on the trees. Before long, they came to the centre of the garden where I had planted the Tree of Life and the Tree of the Knowledge of Good and Evil. Adam, pointing to the Tree I'd warned him about, said to his wife:

👤 Eve, do you see this Tree here, next to the Tree of Life? This is the Tree of the Knowledge of Good and Evil.

👤 What is "evil"?

👤 Evil is the opposite of good. Everything that God made and everything He has given us is good.

👤 This beautiful world and our paradise home are good...

👤 That's right, my darling, but good is also the relation-

ship He has given us with Himself and with one another.

🧑 So good describes our whole existence together in relation to Him and to the world He has given us, and evil would therefore be everything opposite to this life of ours.

👫 Indeed. Good is also the direction we are called to pursue for our life, that is to develop this world...

🧑 ...and to deepen and strengthen the relationships God has given us.

👫 You've got it. Evil is everything that would cause a disturbance in the created order, or a breakdown in our relationship with God or with one another. Evil is to reject good.

🧑 So you think we cannot experience both good and evil?

👫 I don't know if we can but what I do know is that the Lord's will for us is to experience only good and not evil. Just before He brought you to me to be my wife and helper, He said that we may eat freely from any tree of the garden but that we should not eat from the Tree of the Knowledge of Good and Evil. He said that on the day we eat from that Tree, we will surely die.

🧑 So if we eat from it, we will experience evil as well as good and that will make us die?

👫 Yes, as disobeying God's command and thus rejecting His will for our lives would cause a breakdown in our relationship with Him who is the Source of all life.

🧑 That makes sense. So, I suppose *this* tree is all right to eat from?

🌀 At this, Eve took a piece of fruit from another nearby tree, ate some and gave some to her husband. They immediately felt strengthened and refreshed in their bodies and, rejoicing at the blessing of life I'd given to them, continued on their walk until they left the boundaries of the Garden of Eden. Seeing the many large and different animals that inhabited the areas around the immediate vicinity of Eden, Adam and Eve took their first few steps out of the garden, walking timidly side by side. Yet they began to regain confidence as they recalled My words and Michael's explanation about their position as masters over the Earth. Then, walking alongside Eve, Adam reached out and took her hand into his as they continued wandering through the land. And thus, hand in hand, My precious ones took their first walk in the world I had created for them. Every step of theirs was a declaration – an agreement with the words I had spoken to them – and with each step, Adam and Eve felt joy as well as gratitude for the gift of unity I had given them in their ability to understand one another, share their thoughts, feelings and desires with each other and make decisions together.

The animals, recognising the authority Adam and Eve carried, were quick to show their masters respect, each in their own way. As Adam and Eve passed by them, the hooved animals bowed their necks to the ground; those with soft paws either clapped their front paws together or tapped on the ground; the birds fluttered their wings and the insects each made a sound with their wings or with their legs. The couple tried to touch or to otherwise show affection to the animals that greeted them, seeing in the eyes of each one respect, admiration, loyalty and trust. After having saluted their masters, the animals continued about their own business and, observing them for a while, Eve said:

🐾 Adam, I seem to understand the animals even though they don't speak like we do. I can foresee their plans, their intentions and I know what they're saying to one another!

🐒 So do I! See, they're almost like us, Eve – they also think and feel and communicate. Yet their thoughts and intentions are concerned only with the physical world –

🐒 food, drink, shelter, rest and reproduction –

🐒 and they don't seem to give thought to things beyond the material. It appears that the non-physical part of the animals, while similar to our own soul, is made to be much simpler. They also have feelings, thoughts and desires but they're basic ones and are only concerned with their physical existence. It seems that the highest thoughts the animals have are to do with us.

🐢 At this, Adam motioned to one of the monkeys that was sitting on a nearby tree and it immediately came to him. He held it up in his arms and gently stroked its head. Adam continued:

🐒 They seem to understand that it is good for them to have us as their masters, and by seeing how interested they are in us I can tell that they are capable of growing attached to us and to one another. We must use the superior intellect and reasoning abilities God has given us as well as the animals' natural tendency to seek closeness with us in order to help them.

🐒 Like this, you mean?

🐢 Taking a stone, Eve used it to crack open a nutshell that had fallen to the ground under the walnut tree. She then took the nut out and held it towards the monkey who, visibly excited and thankful, snatched it from her hand and ate it up. It then leapt from Adam's arms to the ground, picked up a small stone and tried to crack open another walnut. It wasn't able to as the stone it used was smaller than the one Eve had used, so the monkey began looking for a bigger stone.

👥 Here you go!

🐒 Adam hurled a bigger stone near the bushes where the monkey was searching. It took it, ran to the nut, cracked it open and ate up the contents of the shell. Two other monkeys that had been watching nearby now came under the walnut tree and began cracking shells open in the same way. Every time they succeeded, they jumped up with excitement at their newly acquired skill and waved at Adam and Eve with gratitude.

Thus, the couple spent their first day together in the fields and woods around Eden, helping the animals with their food, shelter and whatever else they needed help with. They taught the larger animals to use their legs to rock the tree trunks back and forth in order to shake off the fruit they couldn't reach, and the animals that could hold things with their paws to use sticks and stones to help them gather food they couldn't reach otherwise. After working alongside his wife a while, Adam said:

👤 Eve, I think what the animals need most is structure in their communities. They don't follow any regulations regarding their life in groups and, while they live fine at the moment, once their populations grow, it will become increasingly difficult for them to live without any rules.

👩 I see what you mean, Adam, but from my point of view what the animals need most is to be taught some basic things like how to build shelters for their young. Baby animals are very fragile when they arrive, and it will save the mothers a whole lot of hassle if they can place their newborns in sheltered places away from the commotion of other adult animals.

👤 Why don't we separate then, so I can focus on setting

up some order amongst the animal communities and you can go ahead and instruct them on how to set up shelters?

🐦 That's a good idea, Adam. I'll see you back here afterwards and we can walk back to Eden together.

🕉 And so it happened. After they separated, Adam called a few of the oldest and the strongest animals to himself. He appointed them as leaders over their animal groups, making them responsible for some of the practical aspects of life in a community, such as the allocation of territories and various rules regarding food, drink, shelter and reproduction. Eve taught some animals that had just had their young to keep them sheltered from the Sun and, while still small, to keep them away from other animals that may accidentally injure them. In the days that followed, the animals that were personally taught by Adam and Eve passed on what they learnt to others, until all earthly animals had received Adam and Eve's instructions on how their life in the world should be organised.

Sharing

First Experiences

🕉 After having finished their work with the animals, the couple reunited again in mid-afternoon. When Adam saw his wife again, he embraced her and said:

👫 Eve, we've only been apart for a short while, but it felt like such a long time! I... I missed you!

🕊 It felt the same for me. I knew I'd see you very soon but I was still thinking about you and wondering how your work was going. I also couldn't wait to tell you about my work with the animals...

👤 I love you, Eve.

🕊 And I love you, Adam.

☸ After a kiss, the couple began to slowly make their way back to Eden. As they were walking, Eve said:

🕊 So tell me, how did you set up the structure in the animal communities? From what I've seen of them so far, they really do look more organised now.

👤 I'm glad you notice a difference. I initially thought about ruling over the animals myself and being the one they'd come to for guidance. But then I realised that would be too much work for me, especially once animal populations grow.

🕊 Oh, yes... When that happens I suppose organising the animals is all you'd be doing all day long!

☸ They both laughed at the thought. Then Adam continued:

👤 I remembered that Michael said he and the other angels could help us with decision-making so I asked him what he would advise me to do. So... Eve, why are you smiling like this?

🕊 Because I also asked an angel to help me with my work!

👤 You did? Wow!

🕊 Yes, but I'll tell you my story when you've finished yours...

👤 All right... So... when I explained to Michael what I wanted to do, he advised me to follow the model that God had set up: a hierarchy amongst the animals. Of course, I should have thought of it myself, but I guess I was so focussed on the need at hand that I needed angelic help to be able to see the solution that's now so obvious to me.

👼 And what happened? What did Michael say to you?

👫 When I told him that I'd like to know about the structure God had set up as a foundation of all community life, this was the dialogue we had:

"👼 Adam, the Lord is all-knowing and all-powerful and yet, rather than ruling over creation directly, He has chosen to delegate some of His authority to individual creatures whom He has chosen as rulers over others. Thus, Gabriel, Heylel and I have been appointed as chiefs over the other angels...

👫 ...and Eve and I have been appointed as rulers over the Earth and its creatures...

👼 That's right.

👫 So rather than ruling over the animals personally, just like the Lord, I could set up individual animals as rulers over whole groups! In this way, I'll only need to give instructions to group leaders and they'll be the only ones reporting to me directly.

Michael, after I've appointed leaders in a few animal groups, could you and the other angels help the animals I haven't seen to adopt the same structure in their groups?

👼 Yes, Adam, we'll help you with that."

👫 And so it happened, Eve. I put several types of animals into groups – herds, packs, flocks and others – and appointed leaders over each one.

👼 And how did you decide which animal to make the leader?

👫 Oh, that wasn't hard at all. The animal amongst the oldest and strongest in the animal groups that first acknowledged my presence with them was made the group leader. It was clear that animal was the one with the strongest senses in that group, as well as being the one who'd be most loyal to me as its superior.

🧑 That's wonderful! You've done a great job!

👼 Thank you, my darling. It feels amazing to bring structure and order where there was none before. Now, tell me about *your* work with the animals. What did you teach them about their young?

🧑 Well, I first spoke to some medium-sized female animals about the kinds of ways they could protect their newborns from harm. I made a bundle from sticks and mud and used it as a new born animal dummy. I then demonstrated what happens to the bundle when a large animal treads on it and when objects fall on it, such as fruit, tree branches and boulders.

👼 How did they react?

🧑 They were very emotional at first but calmed down once I showed them how to build shelters for their young. Some larger animals and a few birds were watching us and, seeing that this was an instruction I was giving to the smaller animals, they began sharing it amongst themselves. I then realised that, while the animals were quick to pass on what they'd learnt to others, my instructions would spread much faster with help from the angels. Gabriel was the one who showed the most interest in my work, so I asked him and the angels under his charge to pass on my instructions to the animals that hadn't yet received them. After a while, Gabriel came back and said:

"👼 Eve, all female land animals, including those who haven't had young yet, have now been taught to take care

110

of their babies in the way you directed. The birds took your warning about the possibility of their young being trampled on so seriously that many of them have made shelters for their chicks, even on top of trees!"

(♀) Wow! You also accomplished what you set out to do. Fantastic work, my darling.

(♀) Thank you, Adam. I enjoyed it too. But I'm tired now.

(♀) So am I. Although I haven't done much physically, instructing even a few animals on how to lead their respective groups well was more tiring than I thought it would be...

(☸) Thus, engaged enthusiastically in dialogue, they reached the entrance path of Eden.

Experiences

Beyond the Physical

(☸) Upon entering their home, Adam said to his wife:

(♀) Let's sit and take a rest by that river over there.

(☸) So, hand in hand, Adam and Eve walked over and sat down by the shore of one of Eden's four rivers – the river that people would one day call the Tigris. It was now late afternoon and the sun's rays were barely piercing through the thick, blanket-like foliage of the trees growing alongside the river. Embracing one another whilst enjoying the scenery, My precious couple began sharing their thoughts about this first day they had spent together as guardians and rulers over the Earth:

👤 Darling, I'd like to tell you about something I experienced today while I was instructing the pack and herd leaders... I still don't quite understand it and I'd like to hear your thoughts.

👤 Sure, go ahead.

👤 Well, at first when the leaders I appointed started following my instructions and taking authority over the other animals in their groups, they kept coming back to me and asking me for guidance. I greatly rejoiced in that as I could see that they trusted me and were being obedient – I was fulfilling my task of being their master and they were following my directions. Then, little by little, as some leaders grew more confident, they stopped coming to me to ask for help. Instead, they began to help other leaders who still lacked in confidence and needed guidance on how to exercise authority over their groups. Seeing this...

🕊 Tears sprang to Adam's eyes as he continued:

👤 ...I cannot describe the joy I felt in my heart. I don't even know if *joy* is the right word! It wasn't a *feeling* of happiness, an *emotion* in my soul. It was much deeper – more like a sense of *completeness*, a *rightness* somehow in the innermost part of my being.

👤 A feeling not that you're *doing* something right, but that you're *being* something right?

👤 That's exactly it! You've felt this too?

👤 Yes. I felt the same thing when Gabriel told me the birds had made nests for their young on top of trees, even though I myself had not given them such an instruction. Of course, I rejoiced when I saw the land animals making dens for their young in shady places away from other animals, but a whole different level of joy – as you said, in my *spirit* –

overcame me when I heard the report about the birds.

👥 How do you explain it? What were you happy about?

👥 I was filled with a sense of profound satisfaction when I heard that the birds had not only understood my instructions but the *reasoning* behind them. They weren't just following rules – they had understood a principle that they applied to their own specific circumstances. They had gained an understanding not only of my instructions but of my *thinking*, and had thus in a sense come to *know me*, as a person, rather than just hearing and obeying my words.

👥 I also felt that those animal leaders had come to *know me* somehow... But what I think was more overwhelming for me was the idea that through knowing me, they had come to *be like me* in a way – in the independence they showed and also in their care for the leaders who were still struggling.

👥 I know exactly what you mean! But I have no idea why we both had such a reaction in our hearts to this. Why don't we ask one of the angels? They're bound to know.

🕊 Adam and Eve looked around to see if there were any angels nearby and saw that Heylel was not only the one closest to them but that he was visibly very interested in their conversation. Adam said to him:

👥 Heylel, could you help us? We were wondering why we were both so deeply affected by the animals' behaviour, having seen that they were not just following our instructions...

👥 ...but were adopting our way of thinking.

👼 I'll be glad to help. You see, you and Adam were created with a purpose...

👥 To take care of the garden and to rule over the Earth and its creatures, cultivating and developing it.

👼 Oh, no, that's the work you've been given to do. Purpose is more to do with *being*, rather than with *doing*.

👥 So our purpose is to *be* masters over the Earth?

🧕 When you begin discovering your purpose, your spirit reacts within you and you sense joy, excitement and peace all at the same time. You didn't sense this when you set off on your first walk as masters over the Earth, did you?

👥 We definitely felt joy when we took up our position as rulers over the Earth but that was a more ordinary kind of feeling. What we experienced when we saw the animals adopting our way of thinking was a feeling from much deeper within us – a feeling within the core of our being.

🧕 That is how your heart reacts to you discovering your purpose, because your purpose doesn't stem from your interaction with the physical world, although it does influence your life in and your relationship with the physical world. Your purpose stems from your interaction with the spiritual world and your relationship with One Being in particular.

👥 👥 God!

🧕 That's right.

👥 So when we experienced this sensation seeing the animals' response to our instructions, this had something to do with our purpose in relation to God?

🧕 Absolutely. Almost everything in creation is designed to lead you to a knowledge and an understanding of your purpose. It was God who used this situation to speak to your hearts about His plans for you.

👥 So, we are called to also adopt God's tway of thinking?

🧕 Yes, and much more than that. As I said, by drawing your attention to the animals' behaviour in this instance, God provided you with a picture of what you are called to be.

👥 The animals don't realise this, right?

No. They don't have the same reasoning abilities as you. But God, in His infinite wisdom, used your interaction with the animals today to provide you with a signpost to His ultimate purpose for creation.

You mean God's ultimate purpose for *us* – people?

All created things, both in the physical and in the spiritual world, are made in such a way as to be influenced by humanity's interaction with God. The way you develop as a species will inevitably have an impact on all of creation.

Is that how important *we* are?

We don't have half as much knowledge or power as you angels do!

The importance of created beings depends not on their personal qualities. Rather, importance amongst God's creatures has to do with His sovereign choice as to which creatures He will bring into close communion with Him.

On hearing this Adam and Eve were visibly astonished by the angel's words, so much so that Heylel felt the need to respond to their reaction:

We, the angels, do not know the full extent of God's plan for people, nor do we comprehend His reasoning behind His decision to give humans the ability to become what He desires for you to become.

What does He desire for us to become?

Creatures who will rise to have a fellowship with Him like no other created beings have.

When Heylel said this, Adam and Eve looked at each other searchingly, to see whether the other had heard Heylel's words too. Eve was the one who confirmed first:

Yes, the moment Heylel said this I again felt that same deep kind of joy and inner satisfaction. Heylel, it's exactly as you said – I experience this only at certain times... You know everything!

🪬 Oh, no, not in the least! Only God knows everything. But He has chosen to reveal certain things to me about His relationship with humanity, so that I can help you in your path that leads to the fullness of His glory.

☯ Seeing their bewilderment, Heylel added:

🪬 It is not something that you could grasp with your mind, even if I explained it to you. I myself do not understand it fully. For your sakes, however, I have been granted knowledge of the way to achieve your purpose.

🜛 You know the way?

🪬 I do. And you know Him too.

🜚 The way is God Himself?

🪬 The way is God Himself and the way is also *within* Him. This is all I can say for the moment – God will teach you the rest. You're meeting Him tonight, I think?

🜛 Yes, we'll be meeting Him every evening.

🪬 It will be during those times that God will teach you personally about your life and purpose, while during the day you'll be learning from your experiences and through your interaction with us.

🜚 Thank you, Heylel.

🪬 It is an honour to serve my Lord by helping the people He has created.

☯ With these words, Heylel left Adam and Eve, who continued to sit by the riverside at the close of day, admiring the beauty unfolding around them and taking in the sights, sounds and smells of the garden. Yet, following their conversation with Heylel, they were now looking at the world I'd made through different eyes. They now knew, albeit only

basically, that the purpose of their lives went beyond their interaction with creation – they were called into relationship with Me, which would form the basis of their life on the Earth and would develop them as individuals and communities in My likeness.

CHAPTER

Adam and Eve's First Walk With God

Life Together

⊛ Although My precious couple did not and could not grasp with their minds the idea that I had called them to something higher than their immediate task of overseeing the Earth, their hearts embraced it, and it was with great excitement that they made their way back to our meeting place when the time came.

When I asked them how they had found their first day of taking care of the Earth, it was Adam who spoke first:

⚭ It was a day of hard work but also a day of joy, excitement and... discovery. Yes, of *discovery*! And discovery of the most intricate kind.

⊛ Intricate?

⚭ Yes, it was while we were going about doing our work in the fields and the woods... But You know all this, don't You? You've seen everything that happened.

⊛ I have, but I haven't heard it told by you. Let's take a walk together in the garden and you can tell Me all about it.

⊛ They agreed and as we set off along one of the small paths that meandered down from the northern side of Eden, Eve began:

⚭ Well, when we parted from You, we first spent some time studying the animals and their way of life. We saw that they were naturally inclined to seek our company, especially the mammals.

⚭ We found great joy in being together and working alongside each other. Eve truly is the kind of helper I needed. She is of the same intellectual capacity as me yet very different in her perceptions and her approach to problem-solving.

So she helps me see things from a different angle.

🙋 We make great partners, God, as it appears that You have made Adam more capable than I am in some aspects, and me more capable than he is in others. So while Adam is physically stronger and is naturally inclined to seek to instil structure and order, You have clearly made me more capable with language and expression, and more predisposed to direct my energies to smaller units, such as animal families and individuals.

👫 Yet, our connection is more than a partnership and our attraction to one another goes beyond the reproductive necessities of our kind. We feel a kind of longing for each other's presence when we're apart – a need deep within us to be together, not for any particular purpose but just to share with one another the life that You've given us.

🙏 That longing you felt for one another when you were each about your own business is rooted in the essence of the relationship I have caused you to be in. While being two distinct persons, each with your own individuality and characteristics, you are in fact *one* – one unit, one entity, a union. Feel free to share more of your thoughts and feelings, My dear couple, as I can tell that there is more you'd like to say both to Me and to each other. Why don't you use song? Music is a powerful tool for expressing those things you may find difficult to express in words.

👫 Thank you, God. Indeed, we will!

🙏 By this time, we'd reached a meadow where the couple took it in turns to sing out their feelings of gratitude for each other.

I look at Eve, O God, and what I see
Is Your amazing care!
She's such a precious help for me
In this life we have to share.

O, Eve, my wife, my gentle friend –
My greatest earthly prize,
You, my darling, my true godsend
Are perfect in my eyes!

To be for Adam, my husband dear,
A helper and a friend in life,
Makes all my inner being cheer
O, thank You, God, that I'm his wife!

O, Adam, my strong and handsome one,
My soul is one with yours, my love!
This life of ours has just begun –
A wondrous gift from God above.

The Angels' Help

⊛ When Adam and Eve had finished their song, I said:
⊛ I'm glad you shared with Me the joy you feel when you are together, My dear couple! Would you now tell Me about your first experiences with taking care of the Earth?

꩜ Faithful to Your call for us to subdue the Earth and rule over the animals, we used our intellectual and spiritual superiority to complete this task.

꩜ And how did you find the angels' assistance in all this?

꩜ They very kindly helped us with the things we didn't understand or couldn't do ourselves.

꩜ Gabriel and his subordinate angels helped me by passing on my instructions to all female land animals. If it weren't for them, it would take me weeks to personally teach each individual animal how to live safely with its young, when hundreds upon hundreds of animals of each species inhabit the Earth one day.

꩜ I was helped by Michael and his group of angels in the same way – they listened very carefully to me instructing the animal group leaders on how to create structure and hierarchy in their communities, and they took these instructions to group leaders who weren't there to hear me personally.

꩜ God, it's amazing how You've made the angels to be so effective in their task of helping us.

꩜ Indeed!

꩜ They used so many different ways to communicate with us and with the animals. While most of the time they appeared physically to us and spoke with us directly, there were times when they were passing on information to us indirectly.

꩜ Yes, I experienced that! One of the times an angel guided me without using spoken words was when I was instructing one of the herd leaders of the larger animal species. I had approached the leader and started speaking to him when, all of a sudden, some of the other herd members, clearly curious to hear the instructions I was giving to their

126

leader, huddled up so close to me that I could hardly be seen among them, let alone heard. At that moment, I sensed Michael's guidance in my mind: "Go and stand on that rock up there so that all the animals can see you." I did as Michael advised me and from that place, I was able to pass on my instructions effectively.

🔮 Eve, was that the kind of indirect communication you meant?

👤 Oh, no. My experience was different. When I was showing the female animals how to build shelters for their young, an angel spoke to me through the mouth of one of the animals and said: "Make sure you ask them to demonstrate to you what they have learnt after you've shown them what to do." At first, I was surprised to hear an animal speak using language and then I realised, it can't have been the animal speaking but one of Gabriel's angels speaking through her!

🔮 Why do you think the angels used this kind of communication with you in those situations?

👤 I think, in my case, Michael just wanted to pass on his advice to me quickly to help me give my instructions effectively in the midst of all the commotion the animals were making.

👤 Yes, that makes sense – the animals do tend to get overexcited sometimes and it can be a real struggle to get them to quieten down! Yet I feel like the angel that Gabriel assigned to help me had another reason for speaking to me through an animal's mouth.

You see, it happened when I was helping the animals we called "rhinoceri". I explained to them that, although their calves are born very large in size in comparison to other baby animals, they would get badly hurt if an adult rhinoceros trod on them accidentally. I suggested that the females should gather large objects – boulders and fallen tree branches – and order them alongside one another, forming a kind of protective wall around their newborns.

As I'd taught the ones we called "hippopotami" the same thing just before I came to the rhinos, seeing that they were of a similar size, I didn't see the need to ask them to demonstrate to me how they would build a shelter – I assumed they'd do just fine! It was as I was leaving the rhinos to go on to another animal species that I passed by a hippo, who had been standing nearby watching the rhinos receiving instruction. It was through that hippo that the angel spoke to me and advised me to ask the rhinos to demonstrate what I'd shown them. When I did, that's when I realised why it was so important for me to see how the rhinos would push the objects about. Rather than using their foreheads and their legs, as the hippos had, the rhinos were using their horns. That was definitely a bad idea! Some of the rhinos were getting their horn jammed in the wood of the large branches they were pushing around, causing a lot of frustration to them. I told the rhinos to use only their legs and the sides of their heads to push objects around, and they quickly and safely learnt how to build the shelters.

The angel speaking to me through the hippopotamus' mouth attracted far less attention to my mistake in not anticipating that the rhinos would use their horns than he would have done had he appeared in his full form to remind me. I'm sure the angel used this mode of indirect communication to preserve my authority before the animals. Could that be?

⊛ Yes, absolutely. In fact, you are both right in your judgment of the angels' motives for speaking to you in these different ways. I would expect that while performing their duties, the angels would find a way to communicate effectively with you in any circumstance, as well as to uphold your authority as masters over the Earth and its creatures.

A Special Kind
of Understanding

⊛ Overall, how did you find the work I have given you – taking care of the Earth and its inhabitants?

ꙮ It was enjoyable but challenging at the same time. After seeing that You've made the animals look up to us for guidance and support, we realised what great responsibility You have chosen to entrust to us.

ꙮ Yet, while this is in itself both thrilling and overwhelming, it cannot in any way compare to the excitement and awe that filled our hearts when we learned of Your desire for us. Your desire, Your ultimate goal is not for us only to be in a *position* of superiority like Yours – that is, not only to be a picture, a reflection, of You – but You want us to become like You in the very core of our being.

ꙮ And not only is this something we wouldn't have even dreamt of being possible, but the way You will achieve this in us is through granting Man access to You that no other created being possesses. You, the unknowable God, have chosen to reveal Yourself to us, humans, in a way that not even the angels know You.

⊛ I'm impressed how well you've managed to articulate what you've learnt! Heylel has indeed done a great job of explaining to you what My ultimate desire for humanity is. And, of course, your intellectual capabilities have made you able to comprehend his words and the ideas he presented to you. I noticed, however, that the depth of perception you just demonstrated was not the same as that which you showed in your conversation with Heylel. What do you think made you able to gain this deeper insight into My intentions?

ᚗ Perhaps it was what we did after Heylel left us?

ᚗ It must have been. Although we were hardly "doing" anything... We just sat by the riverside thinking and reflecting on what Heylel had told us.

⊛ Indeed.

ᚗ Are You saying that just thinking about something makes us able to *understand* it?

⊛ Thinking about something is part of understanding, of course, but it doesn't guarantee it. However, that's beside the point in this case, as I didn't mention "understanding" but rather "perception" and "insight". Understanding has to do with your mind and answers the question "How?" by studying the method by which a given process takes place, either by making conclusions based on observable facts or determining the cause of a given effect through experimentation. These methods can only be applied to created entities.

ᚗ So that's the reason we were at first so taken aback by what Heylel said?

⊛ Yes, it's a natural reaction when the human mind attempts to comprehend something that is beyond its reach – when it tries to understand something it does not and cannot have the means to grasp.

👫 Judging from our experience, then, the "perception" and "insight" we have gained must have to do with our spirit. It's a kind of knowledge that is realised irrespective of our capacity to grasp it mentally.

🕉 Very well put, Adam. It is something *revealed*, rather than *attained*. The latter has to do with your ability and effort, while the former has to do with My willingness to grant you this knowledge.

👰 So this is what it's called – a *revelation*! It's a certainty deep within us that stems not from logic, nor from observable facts, but rather is a simple yet unshakable "knowing" of a given fact or information.

🕉 That's right, Eve. Unlike understanding, revelation is not concerned with the question "How?", but rather with questions of higher existential significance. Thus, while you don't understand *how* I will bring about My purpose for the human race, you have come to know in the very core of your being, albeit very basically, that it *will* happen. Therefore, while you can apply your mind and understanding to learn facts about My actions and My abilities, you can only come to know My character and purposes through revelation. Revelations show you who I am and what My purposes are for you.

👫 So it was as we were sitting by the riverside, thinking about the words we'd heard, that we gained revelation? Revelation comes as we reflect on words?

🕉 Yes, but only when you reflect on certain kinds of words...

👰 The angels' words!

🕉 No, Eve.

After a thoughtful pause Adam spoke out with a sense of achievement:

👥 God's words... Heylel just passed on *Your* message to us – it was *Your* words that we meditated upon and it was *those* words that granted us revelation into Your purposes!

☮ Exactly right, Adam – you articulate it very well. Eve, the angels serve Me and do all things according to My will. Therefore everything they say is to be in absolute unison with the message I have given them. Thus, in serving Me, they are also serving you.

👥 Serving *us*? But they are so much...

👥 ...bigger and stronger than we are! And they're so...

👥 ...glorious!

☮ They are indeed bigger, stronger and more glorious than you as you are now but...

👥 ...they won't be once we attain to Your likeness!

☮ At this, they both first looked at each other and then at Me while trying to wrap their minds around what they had just learned. After a short while, they realised that this too they'd only be able to properly grasp through revelation, and both let out a small chuckle at the futility of their attempt to once again understand My purposes with their minds.

The Word

☮ We walked together in silence for a while after this, Adam and his wife reflecting on everything they'd learnt so far during our walk together, while I was just enjoying their company and taking pleasure in the beauty of their thoughts and reasonings. After reaching a point of conclusion in his reflections, Adam said:

(♀) You said that we gain revelation about Your character and Your will by meditating on Your words. What is it about Your words that gives us this ability?

(☯) A very well-worded question, Adam. Indeed, the question of process is far less significant than the question of causality.

(♀) Yes, it's not so interesting *how* we gain revelation through Your words but rather *what* it is that makes Your words have this effect on us. Eve, would you agree?

(♀) Yes, absolutely! Learning about the processes that make certain knowledge reach our inner being would be yet another glorious picture of Your amazing creativity and power. Yet, learning about the essence of Your words and what it is about them that reveals You and Your intentions to us, would be a glimpse into what You are like as a Person, wouldn't it?

(☯) Yes, Eve, you describe the connection between Me and My words very accurately. My precious couple, learning about the essence of My utterances will not only reveal My nature to you – it will show you what your destiny is in the clearest way possible. You see, My *words* and I are One! My words are My Spirit through whom I effect all of My will. My words flow out of My *Person* – the *Word*, *My* Word, the One whose glory you are destined to partake in! Thus, when you reflect on My words, exposing your mind and your heart to their substance and message, you are in fact communing with the very core of My Being.

(♀) The Word is... *You?*

(☯) The Word is *in* Me and *of* Me. When you reflect on My words, you are in fact communing with Him as My Spirit reveals Him to you, one step at a time, as He sees fit and proper.

⚭ As the Word sees fit?

⚭ No, the Spirit.

⚭ At this, Adam and his wife looked at Me searchingly, as if they'd be able to somehow see the Word and the Spirit within Me if they looked hard enough. I said to them informatively:

⚭ I've chosen to use this humanlike body for Myself only to make the communication between you and Me easier. You wouldn't be able to see My Word nor My Spirit now, but there will come a day when you will not only *see* My Word but My Spirit will enable My Word to come and dwell among you here on Earth.

⚭ Will that happen before or after we've ascended to Your likeness?

⚭ It is part of the path that takes you to My likeness.

⚭ So, through speaking to us Your Word is preparing us for that time?

⚭ Yes, but more than that. It is My Word revealing Himself to you and thus inviting you to begin your journey towards My higher purposes for you. As you expose yourselves to My Word, thus allowing the Word to work in you, and you respond to the Word's leading and instruction, you and the Word will begin to become one, similar to the way...

⚭ ⚭ ...we are one?

⚭ I smiled and nodded in agreement. After a thoughtful, awestruck pause, Adam said:

⚭ It really is just as Heylel said: *everything* in creation is designed to reflect You and Your will, God!

⚭ It is! The way we relate to the animals, the bond you've

formed between us as husband and wife... You are using all these things You've created to show us a picture of what You have planned for humanity.

💑 We saw... we *grasped* this earlier when Heylel first said it to us, but now it seems that we've come to perceive it *more*; we've come to know it in a *deeper* way...

💑 From this, I can see that revelation can grow within us, as more and more of our being is exposed to the insight Your Word carries. Now I can truly see that this kind of knowledge, this *revelation* knowledge, goes beyond reasoning and intellect. The knowledge we can attain in our minds is finite, just as our minds are finite. However much we learn about a given earthly subject, even if it is the most complex of all created things, a day will come when all knowledge about that subject is exhausted – when we will know all there is to know about it. Revelation, on the other hand, is... infinite. That is because it concerns You, God, and You are infinite?

💑 Adam, what do you think?

💑 Well, Eve, we can gain knowledge about God through our minds too, even though our minds are finite and He is infinite. For example, how did you conclude that God already knew everything that we experienced during our first day of taking care of the Earth?

💑 I figured that, since He made us and everything that makes our existence possible, all parts of His creation must be bare before His eyes.

💑 Exactly. That wasn't revelation – that was reasoning. The difference between mind knowledge and revelation knowledge, the way I see it, lies not in the object – that is whether it is finite, like the Earth, or infinite, like God – but rather in the *kind* of knowledge we gain. They are of

135

a different essence. Mind knowledge tells us *about* God; through revelation we come to know *Him*, personally.

⊛ Very well explained. Eve, you rightly sensed a connection between My infiniteness and revelation, but you couldn't quite articulate it fully. I will help you. As Adam said, revelation is knowing *Me* personally, and as I am infinite, you couldn't know Me with the finite part of your being, which is what your mind is, as you correctly pointed out.

ᐱ We gain revelation of You in our spirit. Does that mean this part of us is infinite too?

⊛ No, but rather it is the part of you that is *able* to grasp infinity. Revelation is not about the knowledge itself but rather what it leads to – to connection, to interaction. When you commune with Me based on the revelation you have gained, you connect to Me and I am spirit.

ᐱ I see now! We can know You through revelation in our spirit because You Yourself are spirit – spirit communes with spirit.

⊛ That's right. The fact that you cannot come to know Me through reasoning does not mean that your mind is of no importance – quite the contrary. Remember, you gained revelation by reflecting on My words and this reflection began in your mind. Yet it didn't end there – it was only where it began. The goal was for your spirit to be impacted by My words – the very core of your being – as this is the place your life flows from like springs of water that stream to all parts of your person.

ᐱ This means that although we cannot come to know You through our logic and reasoning, when we come to know you in our hearts, our thinking and our behaviour will eventually also come to be impacted?

⊛ Indeed! It is that impact that will mould you into what I have called you to be, one step at a time. The steps, of course, depend on you.

⊕ In what way?

⊛ You are the ones who must choose to walk the path that leads towards My destiny for you, and that depends on the decisions you make every step of the way. I have already done My part – I've made My decision to invite you on this journey and I've provided all the means through which you'll be able to reach this goal.

⊕ I understand.

⊕ So do I. Thank You, God.

⊕ Yes, thank You for everything.

⊛ As we approached the place from where we'd set off on this first walk of ours, I said to Adam and Eve:

⊛ My dear couple, it was My pleasure to take this walk with you. It was a time most precious to Me. I'll see you both here at our meeting place at the same time tomorrow evening.

⊕ We'll be here.

⊕ I can't wait!

The Angels' Report

⊛ Waving goodbye to Eve and her husband, I left My precious couple in their home, Eden, where they spent the rest of the evening, enjoying each other's company and speaking about the things they'd learnt during our first walk together. Then I said:

� Son, I am so glad We began to teach Adam and Eve about You as the Word today!

☩ So am I, Father. They will now grow to perceive that when they reflect on the things We say to them, they are in fact communing with Me, the Son, as the Spirit gives them revelation.

� In this way, little by little, they will come to know Us as a Trinity and will begin to grasp that they are My gift to You, Son, and that We made them with the purpose that they would one day come to share in Our Unity.

� They will begin to be enlightened about their calling to take part in Our fellowship, as the Son comes to share in their humanity through My mediation. Now, let Us summon the angels so they can also share their experiences with Us and report to Us on their first day of work with Adam and Eve.

� When the angels arrived, they were no less excited to share their first experiences of working with My precious couple. After bowing down before Me, each of the three chief angels related his first impressions:

� Lord, today has been a day of most satisfying work in serving You through helping the humans You have created.

� I am grateful that You granted me the great honour of being the first to articulate to Adam and Eve Your higher aims for humankind. While naturally they were unable to grasp the concepts with their minds, they were nonetheless strongly impacted by the words I spoke to them, and I believe those words will reveal to them that which You have purposed.

� Michael, how did you find the work in cooperation with the angels assigned to you?

� The angels in my charge worked very well, both as

138

a team and as individuals. One of them even found an innovative way of communicating with Adam according to the need of the moment – he guided him non-verbally at a moment when verbal communication would have been too much of a distraction for the animals. I praised this angel for the ingenuity he showed in this.

🕗 Gabriel, how about the angels in your charge?

🚧 One of the angels under my command also demonstrated creativity in his dealings with the woman You created. In one instance, in order to not draw attention to the fact that Eve had overestimated the animals' intellectual capacity, rather than speaking to her himself, one of the angels under my charge advised her through the mouth of an animal standing nearby. Eve immediately took note and corrected herself without any of the animals realising she'd overlooked something so foundational. I also praised this angel for the initiative he'd shown in this challenging situation.

🕗 How about you, Heylel? How would you comment on your work with Adam and Eve in cooperation with the angels assigned to be subordinate to you?

🚧 I and those subordinate to me, having realised that our work is of a different nature to that given to Michael and Gabriel, first took time to carefully plan how we would approach the task at hand. I told the angels in my charge that the most important part of our work was to watch and observe – to study Adam and Eve in such a way as to be able to offer them the help most suited to their needs.

Most of the time we helped the couple without them realising. Thus, when Adam and his wife first left Eden and set off to explore the Earth outside the garden, noting that they were moving somewhat timidly, I and the chief angels under me helped them regain their confidence by reminding them of their position as masters over the Earth. As You and Michael were the ones who had spoken to them about this, we thought it would be best to simply cause Adam and Eve to recall that conversation in their minds.

Similarly, we supposed that Eve and her husband would struggle to articulate their deep heart joy and satisfaction when they saw the animals not only learn from them but begin to adopt their way of thinking, so we assisted them with choosing suitable words to express what they'd experienced. It was after they had returned to Eden that I had my first direct interaction with the couple – when they summoned me and asked me to aid them with understanding their experience.

The nature of our work is such that, unlike the angels subordinate to Michael and Gabriel, those in my charge could not in any feasible way adopt creativity or individuality in their approach to the task at hand. After they saw the depth of insight I had gained into Your purposes for humanity, and having understood the importance of our work with Adam and Eve, the angels became more and more diligent in their obedience to my instructions as the day unfolded. The angels' understanding of the nature of our work, and of the superiority of my knowledge over theirs, brought about their decision to set aside their own knowledge and ideas in the name of accomplishing the task at hand in the best possible way. It is for this action of theirs that my subordinate angels received praise from me.

⊛ Very well, Heylel. Good work, all three of you. You are now free to attend to the other responsibilities you've been given regarding My creation.

⊛ With these words, I dismissed them from My presence as this day of first experiences and of learning, for human as well as for angelkind, was drawing to its close. All of them had made good progress in their knowledge of Me, of themselves and of the purposes I have for creation. All, except one.

CHAPTER

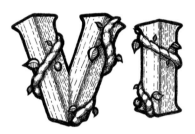

The Path That Led Away From God

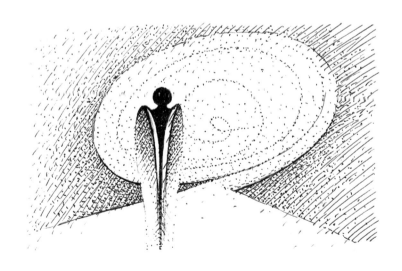

Heylel's Work

⊗ Having dismissed Michael, Gabriel and Heylel after they had reported to Me on their first experiences of working with Adam and Eve, I summoned Heylel to Myself in private. I wanted to share with him some of My thoughts on the way he was approaching his work with the couple, without any other angels being present. When he entered My presence, Heylel bowed down and said:

👤 My Lord, how may I be of service to You?

⊗ Heylel, I'd like to speak to you about your work with Adam and Eve.

👤 I find such great fulfilment in my work, Lord, perhaps because I'm so good at it and, of course, because, of the tasks You gave to Michael, Gabriel and me, mine is the most important.

⊗ Heylel, I would like to talk to you about your attitude towards your work that you just demonstrated. What you said just now entirely encapsulates My concerns about you. I think you should reconsider whether quite so much of your focus should be on your own ability to accomplish the task.

👤 I haven't really thought about my focus, Lord, nor my attitude for that matter.

⊗ The *attitude* with which a job is done is just as important as the job itself, Heylel, while what you're focussed on is the thing that will eventually rule your life.

👤 Lord, *You* are my Ruler! You rule over the whole of creation! How *could* anything else rule over me?

⊗ You're right, Heylel, I *am* the ruler over all that I've

made but that doesn't mean that it is impossible for something to gradually take you over.

🜃 Heylel looked at Me, his beautiful eyes glistening with curiosity as if he was seeing Me for the first time. After a long, thoughtful pause, he said, almost to himself:

🜨 *Why* would anyone choose not to submit to Your will, my Lord? That could only happen if they didn't know who You were – Your power, Your splendour, Your beauty, Your goodness...

🜃 ...or as they come to know more of Me, they discover something in the way these qualities of Mine manifest themselves that is different to what they expected, or to what they would like to submit to...

🜃 Heylel's eyes fastened on Me again and this time he attempted to picture such a situation. He quickly realised, however, that everything he could imagine was based on previous experiences of interactions with Me and thus would not be of any use in the envisioning of a scenario that had no precedent. When his thoughts were at rest again, he asked:

🜨 Lord, you said that I shouldn't focus on my own ability to accomplish the task You have given me, yet it was the angels subordinate to me that recognised my capabilities as transcending any wisdom or skill that they'd seen among our kind. We saw fit that, since I am the most gifted of all, in order for the work to be accomplished to the highest possible standard, obedience to my leadership should be absolute.

🜃 I understand your reasoning, Heylel, yet I am not convinced this is the best way to approach the task I have designated to you.

🜨 You are not satisfied with our results, my Lord?

🜃 As I said, I am very satisfied with the results, Heylel,

but I have made you capable of achieving excellence in the process as well as in the results.

⚜ My Lord, I have invested all my energies focussing on Your end goal for Adam and Eve and have therefore not given any consideration to the process involved in reaching that goal. What would make the process of our work as excellent as the result itself?

❂ The process would be excellent if it took you and those under your charge down the path along which Michael, Gabriel and their angels have already made good progress – the path of growing in understanding of their own purpose. In one of our conversations about your work with Adam and Eve, if you remember, I instructed the three of you to focus as much on this aspect of your work as you do on the work itself. Not making the progress in this area that Michael and Gabriel have is reflected in the different leadership style you have adopted.

⚜ My Lord, my leadership style is only a reflection of the importance of the task You have set me. The fact that my work with Adam and Eve is significantly more important than that of the other two is also the reason why I have focussed more on what needs to be done with the couple than on other marginal issues.

❂ Heylel, how did you come to the conclusion that your work is more important than that of the others?

❂ Heylel was so overcome with astonishment that he could hardly keep his voice steady when he asked:

⚜ Is it not?!

❂ The tasks I gave to the three of you are essentially different from one another, so how could there be comparison, let alone gradeability, between them? And, of course, the end goal of your work is one and the same, which also excludes all possibility for comparison.

🧎 Am I not the most capable of the three to achieve the end goal, my Lord? Have You not made me able to "see and understand the steps humans need to take in order to come to share in the fullness of Your communion"? Did you not say I'd be the one that sees "their needs, what they still lack and what they need help with" and I'd be "the one who will seek specific guidance from You how to best help humanity in this process"? Isn't the gift of music You gave me a mark of my superiority?

🕉 I have indeed gifted you with music, yet not as a token of your superiority but rather to aid you with the task I have given you.

🧎 I have used this gift to further Your purposes to the best of my ability, my Lord.

🕉 You have indeed, Heylel. Your faithfulness with the gift of music amongst the other creatures served as an example to Adam and Eve and endowed them with confidence to employ song to express their own gratitude for the life I have given them to share.

🕉 When he heard this, Heylel's countenance lit up and he exclaimed joyfully:

🧎 Oh, Lord, how excellent! How marvellous! How glorious! Another reason for me to rejoice in my work with Adam and Eve!

🕉 He looked at Me, seeking to detect further praise for his achievement, but his euphoria ceased when he saw My expression and was reminded of the current subject of our conversation. I said to him:

🕉 Heylel, if, with the end goal in mind, you disregard

the process, you may have succeeded in achieving the end goal, but you will have failed to do My will. I advise you to seek counsel from Michael and Gabriel regarding this. Once you have taken steps in the direction of accepting and seeking to understand My correction, you are welcome to come to Me should you have any questions and need of further guidance.

🙇 Yes, my Lord.

🔯 With these words, Heylel bowed down before Me and was dismissed from My presence. Yet, instead of acting on My advice swiftly and seeking to speak with Michael and Gabriel immediately after our conversation, Heylel began to attend to his usual duties surrounding the organisation of evensong – the time the angels devote to worshipping Me at close of day.

Michael and Gabriel's

Point of View

🔯 He applied himself to the task so meticulously that evening that he composed his best melody yet, while the lyrics displayed his finest poetic abilities. This is the song he wrote:

> *O Lord God Almighty,*
> *How glorious You are!*
> *Your throne shines more brightly*
> *Than the choicest star!*

You're marvellous, O King,
We sing in awe of You
Seeing, as we're worshipping,
Your splendour shining through.

It was only after evensong had ended and Heylel had finished rejoicing over the spirit of excellence with which the angelic choir had performed the song, that he asked some of his subordinates to go and inform Michael and Gabriel that he would like to meet with them. Michael and Gabriel responded to the summons swiftly, thinking, since Heylel was employing the angels under his command, it was a matter of urgency to do with their work with Adam and Eve. When they arrived, therefore, Michael and Gabriel were more than surprised to discover they had been summoned in this manner on account of a personal matter. Heylel greeted them using the traditional angelic salute, to which they responded accordingly:

🛐 May the Lord's glory shine on you!

🛐 🛐 And also on you!

🛐 Fellow chief angels, chosen by God, just as I have been, to accomplish His will amongst the humans, I have summoned you in obedience to the Lord's request.

🛐 What is the Lord's request?

🕉 Only when Michael repeated the word "request" in his question did Heylel realise the inaccuracy of the phrase he had used to describe My words to him. A little startled by this discovery, Heylel quickly corrected himself:

🛐 Advice. I meant to say: "following the Lord's advice".

🕉 Michael and Gabriel were amazed by this announcement. "Advice" presupposed interaction with Me on an intimate, personal level, which the angels had only seen Me have with Adam and Eve. Heylel continued:

🙂 The Lord is very pleased with my work with the humans and, in His view, I should pursue the same excellence in the process of what He calls "growing in understanding of my own purpose and design through my work with Adam and Eve". As I have devoted all my energy to accomplishing the Lord's purposes with the humans themselves, I have thus far considered this process less important and have not invested myself in it the way you two have. The Lord advised me to seek your counsel regarding this issue.

🐦 Hearing Heylel's words, Michael and Gabriel began to rejoice and speak words of praise:

🙏 The Lord be magnified, He who sees all and judges rightly at all times!

🙏 Yes, His righteousness and justice know no bounds!

🐦 Heylel was surprised at their reaction, so Michael began to explain:

🙏 You see, Heylel, we both noticed that your ministry to the Lord was becoming somewhat...

🙏 Disbalanced.

🐦 Heylel was even more surprised. Michael continued:

🙏 The disbalance manifests itself in that, while your work with Adam and Eve has truly been of the greatest standard, not having made any progress along the path of growing in understanding of your own purpose has naturally made you focussed on yourself and your own abilities.

🙏 This is the reason why you have begun to compare yourself with us and your work with ours. You think that our abilities and achievements are what will bring us fulfilment in our work with the humans...

But they have – I have found profound satisfaction in seeing the excellent progress Adam and Eve have made on account of my giftings and hard work.

Heylel, when you make progress on the path that Gabriel and I have begun to walk on, you will discover a mystery that the Lord in His infinite wisdom has ingrained into the very foundation of the interaction between angels and humans.

You will be thrilled to learn that our task of helping Adam and Eve serves a purpose for our own existence as well.

At these words, Michael and Gabriel looked at one another, their eyes showing an exultation Heylel had never seen in them before. Intrigued, he asked:

A purpose for angelic existence is served through our work with humanity? How could that be? What purpose is that?

When we witness humanity's ascent to life in the fullness of God's presence, we will gain a knowledge of God that we couldn't possibly gain in any other way.

It is through the revelation that God will give of Himself to humans, leading them to adopt His likeness, that angelkind will see a side of God – a dimension of His character, an aspect of His glory – that is otherwise entirely inaccessible to us, or to any other created being for that matter.

But we, angels, are endowed with far greater capacities than the humans, are we not? How could *we* learn about God through *them* if we are the ones guiding them?

This is the mystery, Heylel! As we, who are stronger, guide them, who are weaker, they will eventually rise to become greater than we are. It is in this that we will see God like we never have before.

We will see God in a new way through the humans becoming greater than we are?

We will come to know God in this new light as we ourselves submit to serving Him in His purpose for humanity.

Seeing Heylel's bewilderment, Michael said to him:

Heylel, you will only be able to grasp this once you turn your focus away from yourself and your own achievements. Just as Adam and Eve grow in their own purpose when they dwell on the Lord's words, we grow in insight when we ponder His acts towards the humans and His purposes for humanity.

After listening attentively, Heylel took a long pause, indicating he was contemplating what Michael had just explained. Then he said with utmost composure:

As you can both see, this is all very new for me. I must now devote time to attempting to fully comprehend all that I've heard today – both from the Lord and from you. I appreciate this time you took to share about your experiences with me.

With these words, Heylel left their presence and flew off by himself to a distant part of the heavens.

Heylel's Conclusions

There, in his mind, he began to go over the conversations he had had with Me and with the other two angels, and to think to himself:

When the Lord appointed me to carry out His will amongst the humans, I devoted myself fully to the task at hand and He Himself noted the excellence of my work. Yet, this excellence was not sufficient to cover over the lack of progress in what He called "the process of growing in understanding of my own purpose". Does not the excellence of my work demonstrate that I already possess a remarkable understanding of my purpose? If Michael and Gabriel have not seen this, then surely the Lord has!

And how could we, the angels, come to know God in a deeper way by working to make humanity greater than we are? Even if it were possible for humanity to grow to possess our capacities, what does our work with the humans have to do with our knowing of God? God, the Almighty! God, the Holy One! God, the Magnificent! Is not worship the only path to knowing God? Have I not been given the gift of music to lead the way along this path?

The Lord said the reason behind the leadership style Michael and Gabriel have adopted is their progress along this path of seeking to gain a deeper knowledge of God through their work with the humans. Having learnt that only some of their focus is on the end goal of our work with Adam and Eve, I now understand why that truly is the case. They simply have no need of an efficient leadership style!

Why is my diligence with Adam and Eve not sufficient to satisfy my Lord? Is not the humans' progress along the path He has for them His greatest desire? Are we, the angels, not devoted to this purpose? And while in God's eyes I am not the most important, have I not been the most productive of the three? Could either of the other two have articulated to Adam and Eve what God's purpose is for them better than I did?

🐦 As these thoughts were going through his mind, Heylel at first did not notice that he was beginning to feel

in a way he'd never felt before. His usual heart disposition of confidence, gladness and serenity became ever so slightly, ever so unnoticeably altered: for the very first time, Heylel did not feel fully accepted and appreciated; there was a place in him that wasn't filled with gladness; he felt like not all was as it should be. Yet, as these feelings intensified, he became aware of them, although he couldn't quite describe them in any way other than that they had been previously unknown to him – as new to him as his experience earlier, when he accidentally used the word "request" instead of "advice" when recounting his interaction with Me. Remembering how futile it is for him to try to grasp something that has no precedent, he thought to himself:

🦊 The Lord... Only He can explain to me what all this is. Yet, before dismissing me from His presence, He instructed me very clearly:

"Once you have taken steps in the direction of accepting and seeking to understand My correction, you are welcome to come to Me should you have any questions and need of further guidance."

He made it evident that my acceptance of His correction should precede my understanding of it. Thus, gaining understanding from Him about these new experiences of mine would also be impossible prior to that.

🐍 Heylel paused at this realisation and looked up towards My throne. It was the very first time he'd looked at the throne without being overwhelmed by joy and without his heart being filled with adoration for My glory. His mind was flooded with the word: "Acceptance".

Listening to every sound of the word as though he was hearing it in his mind for the first time, Heylel proceeded to set out in his mind the most detailed description of My instruction that he was capable of:

🪲 The Lord's instructions always contain within them all that He'd like to communicate – no more, no less – and the words He uses are always precise. To "accept correction" means to submit to it and adopt its guidance in one's attitude and actions. That means obedience. Subservience. Surrendering one's will to His.

☬ As Heylel spoke these words in his mind, the new sensations he was now aware of intensified more inside him, and it was at this moment that he could add another word in his description of them:

🪲 Opposition. These feelings are not just new and different to everything I have experienced in my existence – they are opposite to all things I have ever known. In all my existence so far, everything on the inside of me has reflected only one aim, only one purpose, only one desire... God – His nearness, His presence, His glory. Yet now I see inside myself an aim, a purpose, a desire that points in the opposite direction:

Contrary. Against. In defiance.

Not the Lord's nearness, but away from Him;

not His presence, but where He is not;

not His glory, but His abasement;

not Him, but the opposite of Him:

Me!

☬ Startled by this revelation about the nature of his new feelings, Heylel's lips let out a strange sound – one that neither he nor any other created being had heard before. Being an expression of his internal state of mind, it wasn't only the sound itself that was strange but also the impact it had on Heylel. The sound carried an atmosphere that seemed to envelop him, as if clothing his being with a spiritual substance – a tangible expression of his inner thoughts and feelings. Yet, what this atmosphere seemed to do was not only express those thoughts and feelings through tangible sensations but also amplify them within him. Seeing this effect, Heylel began to ponder in his heart:

🜨 Now this is something new! From what I can see, similar to the way the vocal expression of my thoughts and feelings that sought God and His glory produced a tangible atmosphere reflecting that message and inciting the same sensations in the hearers, the vocal expression of these new opposing desires creates an atmosphere which manifests them.

🜨 Heylel stilled his mind for a moment, letting this realisation sink in. His thoughts then recommenced, now in a more matter-of-fact manner, as he sought to consolidate all that he'd learned from his new experiences:

🜨 The Lord was pleased with my work with Adam and Eve. However, recalling the scarce commendation I received for my work, both from the Lord and from Michael and Gabriel – work which should have, both qualitatively and quantitatively, rendered me the most important factor in the achievement of the Lord's purposes for humanity – I began to think and feel in ways that are in opposition to everything I've ever experienced before.

Now I see that I am capable of vocally expressing these new sensations of mine. And through expressing them, I am able to release an atmosphere that impresses the message of these feelings upon the hearers. In this way, I can invite them to adopt these feelings as their own. It is the Lord who has given me this capability and it seems He is not in any way concerned about the implications of providing His subordinates with freedom to act in ways contrary to His will. I now understand why the Lord expressed criticism of my leadership style – it is completely contrary to His own! Now I perceive a side of the Lord that I hadn't seen before. It is likely the same side as the one Michael and Gabriel said they have come to see while contemplating His dealings with Adam and Eve.

Judging by the outstanding results of my leadership style, I have rightly characterised it as "efficient". Thus the contrary method of leadership could not be described in any other way than as "inefficient". Now I see that the Lord is Almighty and is yet unwilling to use His might to guarantee the efficient accomplishment of the tasks He sets. The Lord is All-knowing and is yet unwilling to use His knowledge to make certain no part of His will is left incomplete. The Lord is All-wise and yet has chosen to make His subordinates able to disobey His commands and defy His authority. The proof that this insight of mine regarding the Lord is absolutely accurate is the fact that, although there is no creature hidden from His sight, but all things are open and laid bare before His eyes, He has not reacted to the opposition to His will that has arisen within me.

The reason Michael and Gabriel are enamoured by God's leadership style is the fact that they do not see it for what it really is, and they disregard its wider implications. They are thrilled by the novelty of their discovery, but do they realise that this kind of leadership style is a potential threat to the efficient functioning of the created order? And who, if not I, could point out this flaw in the current system of governance for the good of the whole of creation?

☮ Reaching this final conclusion gave Heylel a certain kind of satisfaction, which mimicked the joy that, without him noticing, had all but faded from within him by now. It was this satisfaction that empowered him to ignore the fallacy of the reasoning behind his conclusion, which he was otherwise painfully aware of. Conversely, seeing himself as the only solution to the universal problem he thought he had just discovered, filled him with a certain self-importance that took the place of his characteristic confidence, which had now also almost vanished. It was only the loss of his serenity that Heylel was fully conscious of, as he himself actively cast what remained of it off, seeing it as a hindrance to the fulfilment of the mission he had now set for himself.

Sharing Conclusions with Michael and Gabriel

☮ Deeming himself as prepared to embark on the quest of enlightening the rest of angelkind with his newfound revelation about Me and My leadership style, he set off to look for Michael and Gabriel. Upon finding them, Heylel advanced quickly towards them, and seeing the enthusiasm with which he drew near, Michael said to Gabriel:

𐤀 He must have made progress on the path and is now coming to testify about what he's learnt.

𐤀 Oh, what joy it will be for the three of us to now begin

sharing our experiences on this path and helping one another along the way!

🜂 As Heylel arrived, they greeted him heartily:

🜁 🜃 May the Lord's glory shine on you, Heylel!

🜂 He couldn't respond with the same passion but managed to get the words out:

🜄 And also on you.

🜁 Tell us, what have you discovered, Heylel?

🜄 You can see that I've discovered something?

🜃 It's written all over you.

🜄 Well, you're right. I have indeed arrived at a most insightful revelation, with far-reaching, potentially universal consequences...

🜂 Heylel took a pause to see their reaction and make sure he had their full attention. Michael said:

🜁 Yes, please continue. This is all so exciting!

🜄 I have come to the realisation of why the Lord found my leadership style displeasing...

🜂 Another pause ensued as Heylel watched Michael and Gabriel taking in every word of his, while at the brink of the ecstatic outburst of joy that immediately followed his announcement:

🜄 ...It is entirely contrary to His own method of governance.

🜁 🜃 The Lord be glorified, who has once again shown Himself to be All-wise and perfect in His judgment!

🜄 I am indeed thankful for His rebuke towards me as, if He had withheld His correction from me, I wouldn't have reached the conclusions I now have.

🜃 Yes, the Lord's discipline is an expression of His kind generosity and His reproof gives wisdom.

🜨 That's right – whoever loves discipline loves knowledge.

🜨 Michael and Gabriel's joy was so wholehearted, so full of care for their friend and co-worker, that My heart went out to them when they heard Heylel's subsequent elaboration:

🜨 It is true that I gained valuable knowledge, yet it wasn't on account of my love for the Lord's discipline but quite the contrary. The Lord gave me two instructions before dismissing me from His presence: to accept His correction and seek to understand it. I have only managed the latter and that, after refusing to obey the former.

🜨 Michael and Gabriel were so dumbfounded by Heylel's confession that they did not utter a word in response. They just looked at him in disbelief while he continued.

🜨 You see, my honourable companions, while there is knowledge in submission to the Lord and in obedience to His commands, I have found by experience that there exists another kind of knowledge – a hidden knowledge – that one can only gain through refusing to submit to the Lord's will. I have only just begun to walk along that path but I can already tell that the knowledge to be gained there is no less than the knowledge we receive through obedience. Yet it is entirely different to all we have ever experienced in all of our existence! It is *essentially* different from all we know – it is never-seen-before. Isn't that all we have always desired and sought in God – to see a side of Him we've never seen before? A new revelation of His holiness? Well, I have found the *true* mystery, my friends, and it does not lie in a deeper knowledge of God, as you purport, but rather in a knowledge outside of Him – one we gain when we walk away from Him; when we oppose Him and His will. This is true enlightenment.

⊛ Michael, having now recovered from the shock of hearing Heylel's explanation, asked:

🜨 Heylel, why would we want to pursue knowledge along a path that leads away from God? It is God whom we desire and the knowledge of Him, for He is the Source of all glory, knowledge, wisdom and power.

🜨 Yes, the Lord is all these things, yet can you not perceive, even right at this minute, that He is not using His power efficiently? This is the first thing I learnt about the Lord on the new path. Why would I submit to someone who is unwilling to use His power to stop me from disobeying Him? What does that tell us about Him? That He is a weak ruler – not because He is unable to be strong but because He is *unwilling*. Why did He create us with the ability to walk away from Him when He'll be unwilling to stop us from doing so? The answer is simple, my friends. Negligence. Poor stewardship. Absenteeism.

🜨 Heylel, you have completely misunderstood the reasons behind the Lord's decision to create us the way He did and His choice of rulership style. You could only have understood it if you'd walked along the path that we did – contemplating His acts towards Adam and Eve and His purposes for humanity.

🜨 Indeed, judging by the conclusions you have reached, without walking the path you describe, I can clearly see the essence of the knowledge it offers. It is knowledge without understanding. It is insight into process but not into causality. That is why you have learnt about the Lord and His ways, yet you have misunderstood them both. It is a lesser path, Heylel. Perfect knowledge is found only in obedience. Submission to the Lord is the only way one can abide with Him who is the

Source of all knowledge, wisdom, power and glory. If you had walked the path of true knowledge that we have chosen, you would have learnt that what you call "absenteeism" is the Lord's decision to make all reasoning creatures able to have free will – to choose obedience or rebellion. We have chosen to obey Him and have thus grown in the knowledge of the Lord and in closeness to Him, which will inevitably result in Him entrusting us with more insight and responsibility.

⚜ We, the angels, having come forth from God – as have all things visible and invisible – indeed possess great wisdom, knowledge and insight. Yet, as created beings, we do not possess within ourselves insight into causality as there is only one Source of causality – the Lord God Almighty. Your experience of this so-called "secret knowledge" is just another proof of this. While you may indeed accumulate great amounts of knowledge along that path of opposition, know that the further you walk in that direction – away from the Source of all light – the more your understanding will be darkened until you reach absolute futility.

⚜ This process has already begun in you, Heylel. What you call "true enlightenment" is in fact this darkening Gabriel speaks about. The fruit of futility has already been birthed in you – you see things not as they are. This is a natural product of your pursuit of insight into causality – a God-given desire He has endowed all reasoning creatures with – *apart* from the Source of all insight into causality: God Himself.

⚜ It is vanity, my friend. A chasing after the wind.

⚘ Heylel listened carefully to Michael and Gabriel's explanations, fully aware that their reasoning was absolutely flawless. As I said previously, even before he spoke to Michael and Gabriel, Heylel himself recognised the futility of his own logic, both regarding Me and himself. Yet, being able to recognise futility is not in itself sufficient for one to be able to reject it and thus gain understanding. Indeed, obedience is the only path to understanding and that is why I instructed Heylel to first accept My correction and then seek to understand it.

Having already set off on the path of opposition, thinking that he was opposing Me, although Michael and Gabriel had explained very clearly that he was only opposing himself by walking away from his Creator, Heylel's mind was now darkened enough for him to consciously embrace futility.

 If the path of futility is the only way to independence from the Lord – this chasing after the wind – I am choosing to walk on it. After all, knowing the Lord's leadership style, who knows how long the chasing will last?

Should either of you one day rise to my level of insight and choose to also walk the path of freedom, you are welcome to join me... Naturally as my subordinates, since I am the pioneer of this new way.

 As he was departing from them, Heylel looked importantly at Michael and Gabriel one last time. Then, filled with his newfound satisfaction that now fully replaced the joy within him, he exclaimed:

 How ironic for the Lord to call me Heylel – "light-bearer" and "light-bringer". Indeed, I am the one who possesses the light of the new way and, as a friend of creation, I will carry the light to others!

 Looking at Heylel as he flew away from them, Michael and Gabriel responded:

 You are not a bearer of light but one who resists it.

 You are not a friend of creation but an enemy.

⊛ It was then that Michael and Gabriel privately began calling Heylel "Satan", which means "one who resists, adversary". As they had never before seen Me deal with anyone who had rebelled against My will, the two angels could only speculate as to what My reaction to Heylel's behaviour would be. Michael was first:

⚎ The Lord is righteous and holy. He will not tolerate Heylel's behaviour now that he's wilfully chosen the path of opposition.

⚎ He is also merciful and just. He knows Heylel is but a creature and He is bound to offer him the chance to return to the path of true knowledge – obedience and the knowledge of God.

⊛ Michael and Gabriel, having made good progress on the path of the growth and development of angelkind, were both right in their estimations of the way I would approach their friend. On account of Heylel's utter rejection of My instructions, his hardening of heart that led him to rebellion and his attempt to draw Michael and Gabriel down the same path, followed by a pledge to approach others with the same intent, I had to summon him to Myself once again. This time I would rebuke him and give him a chance to repent in the presence of two witnesses, appealing to him to renounce the path of opposition and choose the path where he would find his true purpose.

CHAPTER

Those Who Followed Heylel

Heylel's Second

Summons

⊛ Thus, Heylel was once again formally summoned to appear before Me, this time in the presence of two witnesses – Michael and Gabriel. When they entered My presence, all three angels bowed down before Me, although Heylel's heart disposition reflected an entirely different attitude. I said to him:

⊛ Heylel, you know why I have summoned you to Myself this second time, do you not?

⊛ He bowed down once again but remained silent.

⊛ Heylel, you did not accept My correction but quite the contrary – you chose to embrace disobedience in your heart and attempted to entice others to do the same. You have even pledged to find others among angelkind who would follow you on the path of opposition.

⚘ My Lord...

⊛ He stopped himself, recognising there was nothing he could say in his defence. I continued:

⊛ I have summoned you this second time to issue you with a warning, in the presence of two witnesses, about the direction you have embarked upon, which is a direct result of your reluctance to accept My correction. I counsel you to take swift action and seek to return to the place from which you have fallen.

⊛ I had already signalled to Michael and Gabriel to step back and give us some privacy.

⊛ Heylel, do you remember what I warned you about focus?

⚛ My words immediately echoed in his mind: "...what you're focussed on is the thing that will eventually rule your life."

⚛ But, Lord, did I not confirm my loyalty to You as my only King and Ruler immediately after I left Your presence? Did Your heart not take pleasure in the greatest evensong of adoration I have ever composed?

⚛ I delight greatly in all the songs of praise you have made for Me so far, Heylel. Worship brings not only pleasure to My heart but draws My creatures near Me; leads them along the path of knowing Me and growing into what I have purposed for them. Yet, obedience is a greater act than all the songs of worship you could offer, as disobedience is the path that leads away from Me and works the opposite of My will and purpose in the lives of My creatures. It is your desire for explicit prominence amongst the others of your rank that brought about the changes inside you. It is those changes that you wanted to ask Me about, but you knew that you had to first accept My correction before you could approach Me again. Had you chosen to humble yourself then, to turn onto the path I pointed you towards, the excellencies of which Michael and Gabriel also testified of, you yourself would have made progress along that path, even greater than theirs.

At these words of Mine, regret has filled your heart, yet it is not your disobedience you regret. Nor do you regret not having taken the opportunity to make progress on the path of growing in knowledge of Me and into My purposes for you. You regret missing out on a chance to gain the supremacy over Michael and Gabriel that you so crave.

⚛ It is as You say, my Lord. You see all things.

⚛ You yourself know very well that I have made every

172

creature of Mine with specific a purpose, and that this purpose is instilled into every fibre of their being. You and the humans are the only two kinds of beings to whom I have given the capacity to know themselves, Me and their purpose in Me, and to find their fulfilment in growing in this knowledge and in developing as individuals through it. You were the one who witnessed Adam and Eve's first experience of their own growth in the knowledge of themselves and their purpose in Me. Michael and Gabriel also shared with you the fulfilment they have found in the path I have set out for the angels.

If you, Heylel, who together with all the angels, have been created and called to witness and work towards the fulfilling of My purposes for humanity, humble yourself, seek My face again and turn from the path that leads away from Me, then I will restore you to how you were before.

⊛ After signalling to Michael and Gabriel to come closer again, I said to him:

⊛ Heylel, before these two witnesses now I advise you – remember from where you have fallen, reject the path of opposition and do the deeds you did at first; or else, I declare to you that you will be removed from your position of authority in the angelic realm and the angels under you will be assigned to Michael and Gabriel for the completion of the task I have set.

Upon seeing your desire to return to the path of obedience to My will, Michael and Gabriel will be more than willing to help you along the way. Aid from Me is also, as before, available to you anytime after you have chosen to accept My correction. Is there anything you would like to ask before I dismiss you?

🙏 My Lord has made Himself perfectly clear.

⊛ With these words, Heylel bowed down low before Me and left My presence. I then said to Michael and Gabriel:

⊛ I am very pleased with the way you both handled this situation and in particular the balance you struck between kindness towards your friend who has stumbled, and firmness in what you know to be the reality of his condition.

I have, however, one thing to say to you by way of correction. When Heylel departed from you with the ambition to share his so-called revelations with others, without conferring with Me first, you took the liberty of judging him yourselves by giving him a new name that reflected the direction in which he was heading. I'm not saying that you misjudged the situation in any way, nor that you did not correctly recognise that Heylel had acted like "someone who resists" and like an "enemy" of creation. Yet, judgment of the *person* – done by characterising not their *deed* but *them* – should only be done after I have been consulted.

⚲ We are deeply sorry for overstepping our authority, My Lord.

⚲ Yes, O King, You, the One who sees through hearts and minds, are the only Righteous Judge.

⊛ Having now received a formal warning from Me, Heylel has a decision to make that will determine his destiny: to overcome the obstacle he has set before himself and gain valuable wisdom through this, or persist along the path of opposition and incur My judgment upon himself. Only once you have seen him make his decision henceforth, will you know whether he will continue to be a "light-bearer" – or whether he will become "Satan" indeed.

⚲ We understand, our Lord.

⚲ Thank You for Your guidance.

⊗ Although Michael and Gabriel already knew how valuable it was to be corrected by Me, witnessing the impact Heylel's disregard for My reprimand had on him made them all the more grateful for My correction. Therefore, expressing once more their gratitude, Michael and Gabriel bowed in reverence before Me and left My presence.

Heylel's Choice

⊗ In the meantime, Heylel had once again set off to seek seclusion for himself. Yet this time, rather than choosing a single remote location in which to contemplate the new situation he now found himself in, he had decided to roam around the outer parts of the heavens. The first thing he began to grapple with in his mind was his feeling that something inside him was now different to the way it had been before this second meeting of ours:

⛊ My being in the presence of the Lord and hearing His words seems to have diminished the new sense of satisfaction I had gained after I discovered the way of opposition. The path to independence from God now seems less a product of my ingenuity and more a manifestation of the futility Michael and Gabriel described.

⊗ While considering the possibility that he may have set off on a nonsensical quest for an illusionary sense of independence that couldn't ever result in anything of value for him, Heylel was filled with an uneasiness. It almost completely expelled his newly acquired sense of selfimportance. Dwelling on this sense of uneasiness that he had never before experienced, Heylel thought:

🗯 As the Lord and His words are in absolute opposition to the new path I have discovered, being in His presence and hearing Him speak to me has worked to dispel what I have acquired from the new path. If the Lord is not only able but also willing to remove from me what I have acquired from the path, it shows me He is also able to work in the same way to reverse the changes that have taken place in me, just as He Himself said. This is Him confirming His word to me – I recognise His voice. His loving kindness towards all He has made knows no bounds.

🜨 This thought made Heylel stop his flight and look up towards My throne. At the sight of the glory emanating from My dwelling place, he sensed an urge well up inside him; a feeling he had almost forgotten, even though surrendering to this urge had previously been the sole aim and greatest desire of his entire existence. Recognising the essence of this urge, Heylel thought:

🗯 There He is – the greatest, most glorious Being in all existence... The Creator of all things visible and invisible... The Sustainer of all life... The One who inspires the angelic host... The Desire of us all... And here it is, rising up inside me, this desire for Him that is inside all who see Him as He is. I know that if I surrender my whole self to this desire now – if I bow down wholeheartedly before the Supreme Ruler, renouncing the path of opposition and laying down before Him all my thoughts, feelings and desires contrary to His will and purposes – His glory will shine down upon me and the Creator's hand that formed my innermost parts will restore me to the perfection of His design for me.

🧍 I see the obstacle inside of me, this... stronghold of opposition. It is here, at the core of my being – right at the place designed by the Lord as the point where the light of the knowledge of God resides. The Lord has placed it within my power to choose what to do with this obstacle – whether to dismantle it or to build upon it. To return to my previous existence or to continue in the path of opposition.

⊛ Thinking about his previous existence, Heylel recommenced his flight, yet now heading towards the centre and focus of My creation: the Earth, the home I had made for Adam and Eve. When he drew near enough to have My precious couple in sight, he continued his musings:

🧍 And here is the path the Lord has called me to walk on... That path along which – the Lord has declared, and Michael and Gabriel have testified to – all angelic desire for God will find its fulfilment. Being faithful to the task of helping Adam and Eve ascend to the Lord's likeness on the one hand, and devotion to studying and contemplating the Lord's dealings with humanity on the other, forms the pinnacle of the existence the Lord has ordained for angelkind.

If I, like Michael and Gabriel, hadn't tasted the path of opposition, I, like them, would see nothing but the Lord's generosity in the life He has given us. I would exult in the honour of serving the Lord through serving humanity; of aiding humanity in their ascent to the Lord's likeness; of gaining a deeper knowledge of God Himself that I could never gain in any other way. Yet, the stronghold of opposition that has been erected inside me has given me the ability to see what the others do not see; to ask questions they would never ask:

Why did the Lord give the angels the desire for Him

and then make the fulfilment of that desire dependent on the way we relate to humans?

Why did He decide to make us – the ethereal and immeasurably more capable in all respects – serve them, those mere earthly creatures?

Why are they the ones chosen by Him to ascend to His likeness, while the greatest honour we're given is to observe their ascent?

Michael and Gabriel, not having ever walked the path of opposition, see these questions as futile and their answers as irrelevant. I do not. I cannot. I will not. There is now a part of me that is not illuminated by His light; a part not permeated by the brilliance of His glory, where the stronghold of opposition casts its shadow. It is there that I see and sense and want an existence apart from God. From this place, I see His glory not as illuminating but as blinding; His purposes for us, the angels, not as praiseworthy but as despicable; and His mode of rulership not as worthy of submission but as deserving opposition.

I understand that this place in my heart exists only on the inside of me – it is a perception of mine that is contrary to the outside reality of God, His character and His purposes. In this sense, I agree with Michael and Gabriel that the promise of independence from God that this path offers is indeed a futile one, as there is nothing in the whole of creation that exists outside of Him; and that includes the path of opposition.

Yet, doesn't life flow from the inside? Don't I exist as a being on the inside first and then on the outside?

Didn't the thoughts and feelings that emanated from the path of opposition inside me manifest outwardly? Didn't they envelop me with a tangible expression of the internal atmosphere, which also served to amplify these sensations within me?

It follows that the quest for independence, while futile on the outside, isn't so on the inside. The illusion on the outside is a reality on the inside. The Lord, who is the Supreme Ruler on the outside of me, does not have to be so on the inside. That is all that matters to a creature like me... To any creature, for that matter. The experience of this independent existence upheld by the flowing of that reality from the inside out can continue for as long as the Lord permits. As I said to Michael and Gabriel: "Who knows how long the chasing of the wind will last?"

⊛ With one last look up towards My throne, Heylel made his final decision to take the path that leads away from Me. He began to build upon the stronghold of opposition in his heart, piling up thought after thought, feeling after feeling, conclusion after conclusion – all things contrary to Me, to My ways and to My purposes. This continued until just enough of the light of the knowledge of Me had been blocked by the stronghold in Heylel's heart to give him the confidence to take the next step of defiance against Me: the leading of his subordinates along the path of opposition.

It had so happened that, at the end of their workday with Adam and Eve, Heylel had dismissed the angels under his command with the charge to assemble at the third hour before dawn to receive instructions for their tasks in the day ahead. Seeing that the time for the gathering was approaching, Heylel did one more thing in defiance of Me before making his way to meet with the angels assigned to him: he used the gift of music I had given him to sing a song

in praise and exultation of himself for turning towards the way of opposition:

You took this step of bravery
On the path that leads away,
Now clothe yourself with knavery
To lead your band astray.

Take up the banner of your freedom!
Raise up the horn of knowledge new!
Is there another that could lead them
On the untrodden way but you?

Heylel, Heylel, brightest star of all –
Discoverer of new domains,
Prince and Lord you will be called
Where God no longer reigns!

☞ Heylel sang the song quietly but with great determination to express all that was in his heart, so that the words would carry as much as possible of the atmosphere of opposition that had built up inside him.

Presenting the New Path to His Subordinates

🜨 Feeling strengthened by the song, Heylel proceeded to make his way to the gathering place and, when he arrived and saw that his subordinates had already assembled in expectation of him, he greeted them:

👤 Hello, all, and welcome to our assembly!

🜨 ...to which they all responded in one voice with the standard: "May the Lord's glory shine on you!" Making sure that all the angels who were gathered had their eyes fixed on him, he slowly approached the front of the assembly and motioned for them to gather in crescent formation around him. Standing as tall as he could and with a tone of the utmost pomposity, Heylel began his speech:

👤 Dear subordinates,

It is my honour to be in the presence of such a great number of capable, hard-working and, above all, diligently obedient angels! It is on account of your unquestioning submission to my authority, having recognised my outstanding leadership qualities and superior wisdom, that we have attained to such heights of excellence in our work. So exceptional has our performance been that we received praise for it from the Highest Heaven!

🜨 Having correctly predicted that cheering would ensue at this, Heylel paused until the exuberant shout of joy the angels gave out finally died down and they turned their attention back to his speech. He then continued:

👤 Joy is indeed the most fitting response to the news

that our work has been appreciated. After all, what is more valuable than our accomplishing the task of aiding Adam and Eve that the Lord has given us, to the greatest possible degree of perfection? Your devotion to me as your leader in this great quest has paid off!

An outstanding leader, of course, is not just one who congratulates his subordinates on their successes but also one who is careful to correct them when correction is needed; to warn them about the consequences of their decisions and the events that would come in the future. It is therefore my duty to inform you that the excellence of our performance has been noted not only by the Lord, but also by our fellow workers, Michael, Gabriel and their subordinates. However, after recognising our pre-eminence, rather than responding with the praise due to others who have proved themselves superior, they expressed criticism of the structure we have chosen for our community – one that has placed me, as the most gifted of us all, as an absolute authority over the others.

At first I thought they simply didn't recognise that our strength stems from the structure we have chosen. Yet, now I am convinced of the contrary – it is precisely because they recognised the connection between my leadership and our success that they decided to bring reproach upon our structure. You see, they were impressed by how much better our work was than theirs (which is, of course, understandable), yet rather than seeking to rise to our level by adopting a similar structure themselves, they decided to criticise it. I can even understand that: a structure like ours would only have been possible among their ranks if Michael and Gabriel possessed leadership qualities like my own. Since they do not, the only sensible step towards progress would have been for them to join our ranks and accept me as an authority over them – something they are clearly unwilling to do. It was probably with an aim to compensate for the insurmountable differences between us and them that they decided to bring up the issue of our structure before the Lord...

⊛ Heylel spoke out My name with great pomposity, and assumed a posture similar to the one he used to take before beginning to lead the angelic choir into songs of adoration of Me. This immediately gripped the angels' attention and they turned all their senses to him in readiness to receive light and knowledge about Me. Seeing this, Heylel turned himself fully to the darkness he had thus far cultivated within himself, so as to clothe every syllable of the words that followed with the atmosphere of the path of opposition:

⚕ To my greatest astonishment, although the All-wise Lord recognised that we are indeed far more efficient than the other two groups, not only was He unwilling to rebuke Michael and Gabriel for their misguided judgment of our work and for their lack of respect towards us – their unquestionable superiors – but He Himself adopted their position! The Lord summoned me into His presence, and He used the exact same words to criticise my leadership style that Michael and Gabriel had used. Upon receiving this treatment from the Lord – the One whom I had worked so hard to please – I felt the way you all feel now: unappreciated and undervalued. I had never before seen the Lord act unjustly towards anyone, so having the One I had always known as the Righteous Judge treat me in such a way was a truly shocking experience for me.

However, looking back now, I am thankful for all of this...

⊗ Heylel took a dramatic pause at this point and, seeing that his subordinates were taking in every word, continued:

⚕ I am thankful all this happened as, through it, I saw the Lord in a new light. You see, before this I thought God, as Supreme Ruler over creation, is One who cannot be influenced by creatures. Yet, in this situation, He not only was but, because of Michael and Gabriel's influence over him, He acted in a way that went against what we know Him to be.

When I took time to think over what I'd witnessed, the first thing I realised was that the reason the Lord was so willing to accept Michael and Gabriel's negative view of my efficient leadership style was the fact that He Himself is unwilling to rule in this way. If this were not the case, He would have immediately rebuked the other two for criticising us. Having come to this revelation about the Lord's character, I began to ponder the future of the created world.

What lies ahead for us if the Lord of creation is unwilling to rule with a firm hand? How will creation prosper if our Ruler is only moderately focussed on efficiency? Isn't a reorganisation of the leadership structure of creation necessary for the wellbeing of all created beings?

When I was contemplating these things in my heart, I began to... You see, this may be difficult even for someone with my verbal abilities to explain, but it is so profound and so vital that others also learn about this... And who else is more deserving than you, my faithful subordinates?

⊗ Looking at the angels' mesmerised expressions, he continued:

⚕ While pondering these questions that had arisen inside me, I found only answers that pointed me in a different direction to everything I had known so far – about

God, about myself... about our existence as a whole. These new *thoughts* gave rise to new *feelings* inside me, and the new feelings gave rise to new *desires* – all of these *different from* everything I'd experienced thus far in my life. These new thoughts, feelings and desires have shown me that there exists... a path... a dimension... another mode of existence, that is not centred around the Lord and His will.

⊛ Heylel took another pause here to watch these words sink into his subordinates' hearts and minds. Although they tried to exude confidence in front of their leader that they had full grasp of what he had just related to them, Heylel could clearly see the bewilderment in their eyes, which he proceeded to address:

⚙ I understand that it is difficult for you to imagine an existence that does not revolve around the Lord. All you have ever known and therefore all you have ever wanted has been to be close to Him. But what if I told you that, once you taste what the new path offers, you will see that we, angels, are capable of a greater and more meaningful existence away from the Lord? Furthermore, if the Creator Himself has made us able to walk away from Him, what does that tell you about His attitude towards us? We desire to be close to Him but how much does He want our closeness if He Himself made the path of opposition a possibility? This makes me feel the same as I felt when the Lord joined in Michael and Gabriel's criticism of our impeccable work: unappreciated and undervalued. Yet what made these feelings the strongest was the realisation that the Lord had already declared the value He places on us through the task He had given us to accomplish with Adam and Eve...

⊛ Here, Heylel took another pause, this time strategically, in order to assess whether he'd succeeded in passing on his way of thinking to his subordinates. Upon hearing one angel whisper: "Angelkind is far more capable than humankind...", another rumble disapprovingly in response: "Yet the Lord has appointed *us* to serve *them*...", while a few others nodded their heads in agreement, Heylel, filled with satisfaction, proclaimed:

🜨 Those of you who already see a little of what I see and understand a little of what I understand, know that you are responsible for aiding the others, who have not yet attained to this knowledge, as I have aided you.

You may have all kinds of new experiences as you continue on the new path, some of which may leave you feeling uncomfortable as you withdraw from God – the only Source you've known so far. But you will discover that life away from the Source has its own channels of provision for our needs and, while these cannot compare in strength nor in satisfaction to the Fountains of the Lord's glory, they suffice when you consider the ultimate gains of the new path – freedom, independence, self-determination, self-will, power... Of course, as I am the pioneer of the new path, anyone who joins our ranks will be subordinate to me and to those I have appointed as leaders, but unlike the Lord, I will generously show my appreciation towards all who contribute to the growth of our influence...

🜨 At these words, the angels who had first responded to Heylel's prompts and adopted his new perspective of Me rallied around themselves those who had not yet succumbed to the path of opposition and began recounting key elements from his speech to them. Heylel, masterful instructor that he is, began hovering above the groups and stopping at each to aid the leader in their effort to paint the most critical picture of Me in the minds of the listeners. When insight that would be useful to everyone emerged from the depths of his heart, Heylel spoke it out for all to hear:

🖋 While this is the path of opposition to the Lord – to His character, to His will and to His purposes – it functions within the created order, following the same principles. So far in our existence we have found strength, inspiration and meaning in drawing close to God through worshipping Him and speaking in adoration of His qualities. Therefore, setting our thoughts away from God towards the path of opposition and refusing to worship Him is a way in which we will grow in the new path. Regarding God's qualities, while we cannot with any feasibility speak in opposition of His power, His beauty and His glory – those qualities that are clearly perceived by all – we can point in criticism of those aspects of God that are not seen, and that you yourselves now know to be not all perfection, such as His intentions and the way He has chosen to act towards His creatures.

As I persevered in these disciplines, I found that what had its beginnings within me as a small stronghold of opposition began to grow and to block out the light emanating from God towards me. From what I see, however, the growth of opposition has thus far only begun to obscure God's internal qualities for me – I still clearly see His power, His beauty and His glory, and although my desire for closeness with Him has diminished, I still have a long way to go before I can be completely free from my natural inclinations towards Him. If I experience such a struggle, as the most gifted of all angelic beings, then *your* struggle will be even greater. Yet with a leader such as myself, who is devoted to helping you advance in the new path of freedom, you will eventually succeed in breaking free from all bonds that have kept you dependent on the Lord.

⊛ Heylel continued lecturing the crowd and aiding the leaders in this way, until all his subordinates had made progress along the path that leads away from Me. Some made great progress while others only took a few steps forward, yet the hearts of all were now infiltrated by the atmosphere of opposition that oozed from Heylel's heart.

Heylel's Third

Summons

⊛ It was after this that I summoned Heylel to Myself the third time, and this time together with his entire troop, as none of his subordinate angels had made any effort to resist their commander. This third and final meeting of Mine with Heylel regarding the path he had taken was conducted in the presence of all heavenly angels. Heylel and his angels' entrance into My presence was met with a stupefied murmur on the part of Michael, Gabriel and the angels under their charge, as the summoned troop made no outward sign of reverence for Me. I motioned for Heylel and his subordinates to gather directly in front of Me. Michael, Gabriel and the angels under their charge took their places to My left and to My right, respectively. Then I began:

Heylel, it is with greatest displeasure that I have had to

summon you to give an account for your actions this third time, after you chose to ignore My counsel and warning the previous two times. You had no regard for My words to turn away from the path you had set out upon. You despised Michael and Gabriel's testimony that true fulfilment for angelkind can be found only in your contemplation of My dealings with humanity. You wilfully hardened your heart against Me, Heylel. Now, you have cunningly steered your subordinates also towards the path of opposition – the very ones you were appointed to lead into a deeper knowledge of Me through your work with Adam and Eve.

In the presence of the whole angelic host, I am hereby extending a third and final appeal to you, for your sake and for the sake of those whom you have misled. Will you renounce the path of opposition and make your way back to the path of obedience to My will, wherein lies the fulfilment of all My creatures' needs, desires and purposes?

Heylel responded in the hearing of the whole congregation, making a dramatic pause after each word:

🜨 I... will... not.

🜩 Then, turning to his subordinates I asked:

Will you renounce the path of opposition and make your way back to the path of obedience to My will, wherein lies the fulfilment of all My creatures' needs, desires and purposes?

Knowing that they were still very much attracted to My glory, Heylel's angels kept their eyes off Me and tried to keep their focus on their leader, to whom their hearts were now bound by the cords of opposition. Then, to the greatest bewilderment of the rest of the angels, they responded in one voice: "We will not."

191

That being so, in the hearing of all here present, I declare that you, Heylel, and all your subordinates, shall no longer be part of My angelic host. You shall hereby be stripped of all privileges connected to serving Me, and your access to My glory shall be removed from you. You will roam the heavens as stars without light until you renounce your ways.

After pronouncing My judgment on Heylel and his subordinates, I motioned to the other angels to remove from them their mantles of service and escort them out of My presence and the presence of the heavenly host. Then two angels, one from Michael's and one from Gabriel's troop, took up their positions in the proximity of My throne to keep Heylel and his subordinates away from My glory, which had thus far been their source of vigour, luminosity and delight.

Thus, from then on, Heylel and his angels began to roam the heavens without purpose and, separated from My glorious Fountains, they started to experience a drought in their beings they had never experienced before. This began to manifest itself outwardly in their appearance – their brilliance started to grow dimmer and the beauty of their countenances was marred by an ever-intensifying expression of desperation. During their gatherings, Heylel assured them that they had now gained their freedom from Me; that they were now free to serve him and themselves, and that soon, they would find the same fulfilment in the path of opposition that they had found in My glory, in their worship of Me and in their work with the humans. But before long, they could no longer ignore the difference between their own existence and that of the other angels. They witnessed the air of serenity and delight that radiated from them, both after their adoration of Me and receiving from My glory, and after returning from

their work with Adam and Eve. Some of Heylel's angels even approached the other angels with the intent of trying to take in some of the glory that emanated from them, but without success.

Heylel had almost fully overcome his need to worship Me, but his subordinates found it very difficult to resist this urge inside them as they saw My beauty, My glory and My splendour, and on account of the lack they were now experiencing having been denied access to My glory. He had hoped that through refraining from worshipping Me and seeking to advance along the new path through speaking critically of My internal qualities, the stronghold of opposition would grow in each one to the extent of being able to block out My visible qualities. However, soon it became clear that he and his chief leaders would have to take new steps in the direction of opposition if they were to retain control of their troop in the long run; to find fulfilment in their existence; to fill the void that was growing in them the longer they spent in exclusion from Me, from My purposes and from My community.

CHAPTER

THE NEW STEPS
HEYLEL TOOK

Seeking Fulfilment

◈ Heylel hardened his heart even further. Seeing the predicament he was in, he frequently sought solitude. At those times, he engaged all his faculties in an endeavour to find a solution to the problem of the growing frustration in him and, despite their attempts to conceal it, amongst his troop. One such instance was decisive for him, or so he thought. When musing over the situation they were in, he recounted:

◈ The stronghold of opposition within us has grown to a point of casting a shadow tall enough to block the light of the Lord's internal qualities but, despite all our devotion to the current disciplines, it has ceased to grow. It is clear that our refraining from worshipping the Lord and our uncovering of His real motives can only take us so far along the path of opposition. While we are indeed free from His control externally, we remain bound to our need of Him on the inside. Dwelling in such close proximity to the Source of all pleasure and purpose while our needs and desires remain unfulfilled, it is only a matter of time until my subordinates succumb to the desire to worship God. What is more, they see, day by day, Michael's and Gabriel's angels return from their work with Adam and Eve, filled to the brim with the joy and satisfaction that the task itself provides, gloriously clothed with newer and more intricate beauty as an outward manifestation of their gains within. Riches... glory... splendour... all gains from the labour amongst the humans.

But whose labour?

Theirs?

Who should receive praise and profit from the fruits of

labour – the one who devises the strategy for the work and whose subordinates follow their instructions impeccably, or those who merely walk in their steps? I was the one who invested hours and hours into studying the humans. I was the one who birthed the vision for how we should approach our work among them. I was the one who was recognised by the angels under my charge as the supreme authority in all questions pertaining to the task of aiding Adam and Eve to ascend to the Lord's likeness. The angels I instructed were those who provided the best model for the work that needs to be done with Adam and Eve.

If the angels under Michael and Gabriel experience such satisfaction from the labour whose very inspiration originated from me, how much more fulfilled will my subordinates be if they begin to relate to me – the source of inspiration and wisdom that is unparalleled among creatures – in a way that fully reflects my qualities? So far they have only expressed their respect of me, but I am worthy of more... of reverence... of admiration...

⊛ Heylel stopped his thought flow there, knowing that he was about to enter into a completely new depth of the realm of opposition – a point of no return. He looked up at My throne, knowing it would be the last time he would see the reality of who I am: he had discovered the way the stronghold of opposition within him would grow enough to cast a shadow over My power, splendour and glory. It was also the way one of the inherent needs of his subordinates would be satisfied:

 They shall worship ME! They shall bow down to ME! They shall sing MY praise!

⊛ With this resolution in place in his heart that made

the stronghold inside himself rise further, Heylel made his way to the place in the outskirts of the Heavens where his subordinates usually gathered. When they saw their leader approach, the angels assembled themselves around him in expectation to hear what new things he had to share with them about the way of opposition. Positioning himself in front of them, Heylel took up his usual pompous posture. Yet this time, there was an element in the atmosphere he carried, which the angels immediately registered as reminiscent of their life before they'd set off on the path of opposition – something that promised fulfilment of their innermost needs. Seeing that his subordinates had assembled around him with a new sense of expectation, Heylel began his speech:

🔥 My fellow comrades, in the quest for a life of independence for angelkind, I would first like to congratulate all of you for your perseverance in the new path, and for your patience during this time in which I have been formulating a strategy for our next step along the way. It has been a period of testing of your loyalty towards me and I am pleased to say that you have all proved yourselves worthy followers of mine. It is my greatest joy to announce to you that I, the one whom you all unanimously exalted as your leader – based on the unquestionable superiority that I possess over all of you in all possible respects – have found the solution to the temporary predicament you find yourselves in with regard to your intrinsic needs following our expulsion from the Lord's community. It is also the very thing that will make the stronghold of opposition grow inside you to such an extent as to make the Lord's outward qualities no longer be a stumbling block for your progress along the path that leads away. Of course, it is clear to all of us that this reality will exist only in our own selves, but as we have chosen to walk away from the life outside that path, why should the reality of that life be of any account to us? All that will matter will be the reality inside us as we progress deeper and deeper into the realm that promises to deliver us from our dependence on the Lord. As we express the reality inside us, it will also grow to be a reality to our outward senses.

You see, all reasoning creatures the Lord has made have an innate need to worship and, of course, the One who has made all things that exist is the most natural recipient of this act. Their worship of Him flows from within themselves, without reasoning or understanding whether He truly deserves it. Words like "holy", "glorious", "worthy" come out of their mouths as a response to what their senses perceive of Him – His holiness, His glory and His worth.

We, on the other hand, having tasted of things contrary to God and having found them to offer what servitude to the Lord never could – freedom and self-determination – have reasoned and have understood that the Lord is not deserving of our worship. In this way, we have shown ourselves to be superior to those who have no perception of the new path. Therefore, we deserve to worship someone who reflects those things which we have discovered to be of value – one who embodies the new path and all that it offers...

⊕ The angels were stunned by these words. They not only communicated Heylel's cunning suggestion but also carried the atmosphere of the new depth of opposition to Me and My purposes that flowed out of Heylel's heart. This profoundly greater manifestation of the substance of opposition beckoned the hearts of the angels under Heylel's charge to deeper surrender. After taking a few moments to consider the implications of the act they were about to commit, their minds recalling mere glimpses of their life before, skewed by their leader's futile reasonings that had now become their guiding light, one by one they began to bend their knees before him. They saw that the stronghold of opposition within them had indeed risen further through this act. They experienced a certain relief from the sense of emptiness they had felt since ceasing to worship Me. And they all joined together in the song that the chiefs among them had begun to sing:

Heylel, Heylel, Heylel,
The wisest, strongest, highest one!
O tell, O tell, O tell,
His splendour brighter than the sun!

He is the lord who set us free
From servitude that had no end,
Through him our eyes were made to see,
Our hearts on him shall now depend!

The Depths of Futility

⊗ While the angels were singing to him, Heylel turned his whole being towards their worship, knowing that in receiving the praise that belongs to Me, he would make great progress along the new path. Every word of theirs served as a building block on the stronghold of opposition inside him. By the end of the song he realised that, in the place in his heart from where he could previously see My glory and power, he now saw an image of himself. Gazing at the beauty of his own image now, with a heart filled with opposition, the wisdom that had been his renown descended to a new depth of futility as he said in his heart:

⚕ I will ascend to heaven;
I will raise my throne above the stars of God,
And I will sit on the mount of assembly
In the recesses of the north.
I will ascend above the heights of the clouds;
I will make myself like the Most High.

⚘ Scarcely had these thoughts finished painting themselves on the canvas of his mind that he motioned to his subordinates to gather around him, and began giving them orders to prepare to rally against Michael's and Gabriel's angels. His subordinates, inebriated by the new sensation their worship of Heylel brought, which had now replaced the emptiness inside them, had forgotten what true satisfaction felt like. And they embarked upon executing their commander's orders.

The First Angelic

Battle

☯ The first angels Heylel's subordinates attacked were those assigned to guard the way to My glory. They charged at them with calls of, "Heylel is Lord of all!" and, "Reject your Lord and accept the path of freedom!". Michael's and Gabriel's angels immediately came to their defence and a fierce battle ensued between the two sides. Although there were two angels on Michael's and Gabriel's side for every one on Heylel's, the sides were initially more or less equal in strength due to the sheer shock Michael's and Gabriel's angels felt under such an unexpected attack by their fellows.

While the angels under their charge were engaged in the fighting, the three chief angels stood behind them as a sign of support for them. It was then that Heylel roared in the hearing of all those engaged in battle:

🔥 The All-knowing Lord has foreseen this battle just as He foresaw the path I'd choose for myself and for my subordinates. Yet not only has He once again decided to not prevent this event from occurring, but He is even now unwilling to intervene with His Almighty strength to deal a decisive blow against us, who have attacked the rest of angelkind! Are you still blind to His attitude towards you, angels? Do you still not see that He is no friend to angelkind? Do you still not recognise that I am the only one who can lift us up to the existence our great kind deserves?

☯ Hearing their leader speak, Heylel's subordinates not only listened attentively to every word he said but turned

their whole hearts to receive more from the atmosphere of opposition his words carried, knowing that it would empower them against their opponents.

Michael and Gabriel felt the need to respond to Heylel's words, but not so much for the sake of the angels under their charge. By now, they had all made significant progress on the path of growing in the knowledge of Me. Rather, their response was a final attempt to speak reason into those who had descended into futility:

🕊 If you had walked the path of the true knowledge of the Lord, you would have learnt that He has given us free will – we are able to remain His loyal servants and we are able to choose to walk away from Him.

🕊 This rebellion has occurred within the ranks of angelkind and the Lord would not intervene in our affairs until He has seen a practical manifestation of our will in this situation. By resisting those who have rebelled against our Lord, we have shown that we will not tolerate such behaviour amongst our ranks.

🕊 We have demonstrated what our will is – to worship and serve only the Lord Almighty, Maker of Heaven and Earth – even if that means having to be separated from those of our kind whom we considered friends not so long ago.

🕊 It is now only a matter of time before the Lord acts in His power to purge our ranks of all those who have attempted to draw us away from the only Source of life and purpose for angelkind.

🕊 A few subordinates of Heylel's, who still had substantial vision of My glory inside them, pondered these words in their hearts. "Could Michael and Gabriel be right? Could it be that we have made the wrong decision?" However, none of them showed any interest in finding the answers to these questions; the image they had of My character was now entirely warped and their senses had no memory of the perfect fulfilment, joy and serenity that used to flood their hearts when they were worshippers of Me. The only thing they were aware of was that, if they made steps back towards Me, they would lose the feeling of satisfaction they had acquired from worshipping Heylel, which had taken the place of the emptiness that had overwhelmed them after being banished from My service.

It wasn't long before Michael's and Gabriel's angels gained the upper hand in the fighting. Yet, despite seeing that their quest to gain control of the Heavens was a lost cause, the aggressors refused to submit themselves to Michael and Gabriel's authority. Following this last, decisive moment when they hardened their hearts to the prospect of renouncing the path of opposition and returning to Me, it was time for Me to intervene and restore order to the Heavens.

Judging the Rebels

🕉 I arose with My presence in the midst of the conflict between the two sides, at which all fighting ceased instantly and all eyes were fixed on Me. I then clothed Myself with retribution and addressed the leader of the rebellion:

🕉 Heylel,
You had the seal of perfection,
Full of wisdom and perfect in beauty.

You were in Eden, the garden of God;
Every precious stone was your covering:
The ruby, the topaz and the diamond;
The beryl, the onyx and the jasper;
The lapis lazuli, the turquoise and the emerald;
And the gold, the workmanship of your settings
and sockets, was in you.
On the day that you were created
They were prepared.
You were the anointed cherub who covers,
And I placed you there.
You were there in My glorious presence;
You walked in the midst of the stones of fire.
You were blameless in your ways
From the day you were created –
Until unrighteousness was found in you.
By the abundance of your trade
You were internally filled with violence,
And you sinned – for sins are all acts done in defiance
of My will and purposes;
Therefore I am casting you as profane
From the place where My glory resides.
And I am destroying you, O covering cherub,
From the midst of the stones of fire.
Your heart was lifted up because of your beauty;
You corrupted your wisdom by reason of your
splendour. I am casting you to the ground!

🜂 After these words, I spoke into being the place I had
planned would exist as one entirely devoid of the sense of
and access to My presence, My influence and all that flows
out from Me:

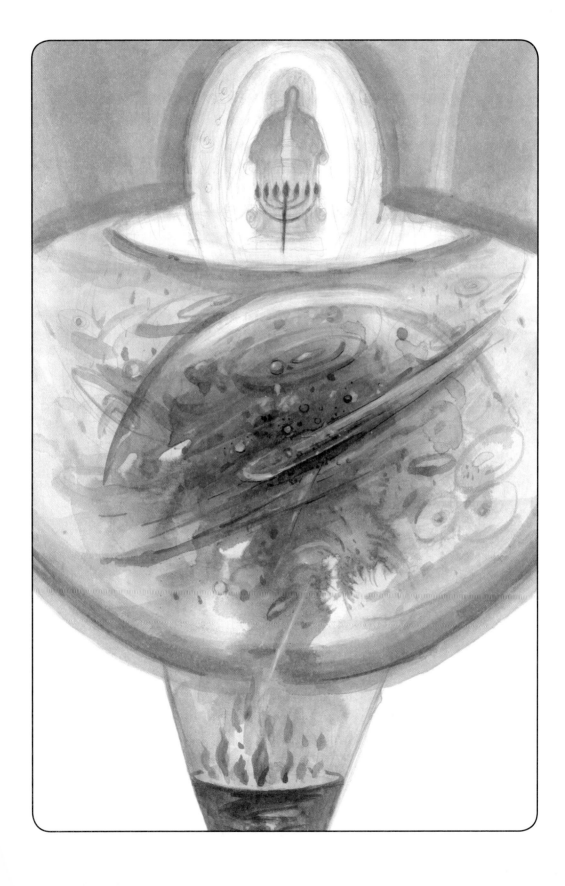

⊛ Let there be a place where all those whose hearts are set in opposition will receive just retribution for their sins – for their acts done in defiance of Me and My will! It shall be the destiny of all rebels.

This place shall be called Hell and the pit. My dwelling place is the highest in all of creation, so let Hell be the lowest. My dwelling place is over and above all of creation, so let Hell be below and underneath all things. My dwelling place is the Heavens, so let Hell be a pit. Fountains of eternal bliss flow in the midst of My dwelling place as a reward for those who are faithful to Me, so let there be in the midst of Hell a fiery lake of eternal punishment. Let it be a place of eternal death for all those who reject Me, the Source of all Life. Let it be the place of eternal darkness for all those who reject Me, the Source of all Light. Let it be a place of eternal restlessness for all those who reject Me, the Source of all Peace. Let it be a place of eternal craving for all those who reject Me, the Source of all Satisfaction. Let it be a place of eternal torment for all those who reject Me, the Source of all Pleasure.

⊛ Then, turning to Heylel, I said:

⊛ You who were called Heylel – "light-bearer"
and "light-bringer" – have become
Satan – "oppositioner" and "adversary"!
Therefore I am bringing fire from the midst of you;
And it will consume you!

⊛ I then reached into the depths of Heylel's being, wherein the seed of the path of opposition lay, and bound the seed inside him to Hell. This immediately brought all those surrendered to his authority under the same fate. Then I said:

⊛ I will turn you to ashes on the Earth
In the eyes of all who see you.

All who know you
Will be appalled at you;
You will become terrified
And you will cease to be forever.

☗ I then took Satan and cast him and his angels from Heaven, Hell-bound, down to the Earth. I removed from them all ability to perceive My glory so that, while they might enter into My presence, they would no longer be able to access My glory, nor see My face.

At the execution of My judgment on Satan – he whom Michael and Gabriel had not so long ago called Heylel, their friend and fellow worker – they exclaimed in lamentation:

🕰 🕰 How you have fallen from heaven,
O star of the morning, son of the dawn!
You have been cut down to the Earth,
You who have weakened the nations!
You will be thrust down to Sheol,
To the recesses of the pit.

☗ Then, all the angels who remained in Heaven began to sing a song in praise of My justice:

The Lord is Righteous and His justice sure!
He has purged from angelkind
Those whose hearts became impure
By their leader's darkened mind.

That angel, Heylel,
That bearer of light,
Is he who thus fell
From Heaven tonight.

Praise the Lord, Almighty, King!
All praises to His Holy Name!
Judgment He did swiftly bring
And clothed His enemies with shame.

Seeking Purpose for

Existence

⊛ It took Satan and his fallen angels a while to overcome the shock of My judgment against their rebellion, as their darkened minds had made them believe that I would tolerate their conduct indefinitely. After they all finally came to terms with their fate, Satan assembled them around himself one evening and began to deliver a speech on the future of their existence:

☗ Dear fellow oppositioners, while our attempt to gain control of the Heavens has indeed been unsuccessful, I am confident that in our foremost quest – for independence from the Lord and from His influence – we have in fact made great gains! The Lord has Himself removed from us all perception of His grandeur and thus none of us will any longer struggle with thoughts and desires for our former way of life as His worshippers. Naturally, this advancement for us is yet another direct product of my brilliant leadership...

⊛ Satan paused here, expecting his angels to respond to this last comment with cheering and praise for him. When they saw his anticipation, some of the chief fallen angels did

make an attempt to initiate a song of praise, but the overall enthusiasm for it was insufficient in Satan's eyes. He looked at the assembly sternly and said:

🛐 Is it that you no longer see me as worthy to receive your worship? Am I not still the one who has shown himself to be gifted in all respects far above all of you? Am I not the one without whom you'd still be slaving around the Lord and His feeble humans? Well, if you do not deem me worthy of your worship on account of my sheer superiority and leadership, then you will worship me on account of your fear of me!

🜨 As he said these words, Satan, whose heart had already embraced the new depths of darkness and death that flowed from the midst of him, transformed his appearance in the sight of the assembly. The light that used to emanate from his person and had begun to fade since I removed the oppositioners' access to My glory, was suddenly fully dimmed and replaced by a darkness that cast a shadow all around him. The beauty of his countenance was smeared by a grimace that reflected the anger, bitterness and cruelty that had now taken over his entire inner being. His eyes were fully blackened and incited terror in those that dared to look at them for any length of time. Then, suddenly turning towards two of his subordinates, he took into himself some of their strength, which made him almost twice the size of the other fallen angels, leaving the two swaying with fatigue in the midst of the crowd. To the horror the other angels reacted with when they witnessed this, Satan responded threateningly:

🛐 As you can see, as a pioneer in the way of opposition, I have my ways of inflicting torment on any and all who dare to challenge my authority or refuse to bow down to me! Let me warn you that even these abilities of mine cannot compare to the torture of the flames of Hell and the lake of fire that shall be our eternal punishment, when the time comes for the Lord to execute His final judgment on us. I thus trust that your judgment of the predicament you all find yourselves in will help you make a sober decision about whether refusing to worship me is truly a viable option for you in this present state.

⊛ Witnessing the power Satan had gained for himself and hearing the threats he made, the fallen angels, both in awe and terror of him, began to bow down before him in worship. As they worshipped their transformed leader, they too began to change in outward appearance so they resembled Satan himself, taking up the same image of terror and darkness, while their hearts were consumed with the same anger, bitterness and cruelty that now filled them with hellish satisfaction. Upon seeing their transformation, Satan exclaimed:

👥 See how far we've come, oppositioners! Not only have we made great progress in opposing the Lord's character through our personalities, but our very appearance has now become the opposite of what He had designed for us! The path of independence remains the same for us, comrades – resistance, defiance, rebellion!

You will be pleased to know that on account of my wholehearted devotion to the pursuit of personal growth in the path of opposition, my mind has expanded in its capacity to conceive plans for our next steps along the way – both in terms of craftiness and speed. Thus, in this short time that we have been on the Earth, I have already engendered the perfect plot that will not only help us advance in our quest for exalted angelic existence, free from the constraints of dependence upon the Lord, but will serve to put off the Lord's final retribution for our rebellion for an indefinite period of time. The good news is that, if the plot succeeds, it will also largely depend on us how much longer our final destruction will be postponed for...

⊛ Upon hearing this, the fallen angels fell silent before him and focussed all their faculties on grasping the plan that Satan unfolded to them:

👥 Since we are created beings, we cannot escape all aspects of the Lord's design for us, as we saw in our inability to overcome our need to worship. The way we circumvented this obstacle in our path was through redirecting our worship from the Lord to another object – one who has proved himself to be a better friend to angelkind...

⊛ After a few calls of praise from the fallen angels – "Satan, Lord of angelkind!" and, "Glory, majesty and power to you!" – he continued:

👥 In the same way, we cannot overcome the need to have a purpose for our existence. The Lord's original purpose for us was threefold: to serve Him; to be witnesses of humanity's ascent to the Lord's likeness and, through that, to grow in our own knowledge of God; to serve humans by aiding them in this path. You are all aware now that our progress on the new path is dependent on our practical advancement in opposition to the Lord and His will. It is therefore more than obvious that the next step in our pursuit of a meaningful life in opposition to the Lord lies in our defiance of His will regarding angelkind's interaction with Adam and Eve.

👥 The Lord's will for angels is to serve humanity in their ascent to His likeness, so we will actively promote the opposite process.

The Lord's will for angels is to be witnesses of humanity's ascent to His likeness and thus to grow in knowledge of Him themselves, so we must advance in the knowledge and power of opposition to the Lord when we become witnesses of humanity's downfall.

The further humanity falls, the greater will our power be!

⊛ At this final proclamation, the fallen angels exploded into a frenzy of praise for the evil mastermind that Satan had grown to be. After letting the crowd chant his name for some time, Satan motioned for them to stop and directed a question towards the chiefs:

🏯 Do any of you conceive of the connection between our acting to draw Adam and Eve away from the Lord's will for them and the time the Lord will allow us to exist in a state of opposition, before finally annihilating us?

⊛ One of the most prominent leaders in his entourage responded:

"The Lord, albeit a Being not dependent on anything outside Himself, has clearly attached Himself to humankind for reasons we cannot possibly grasp. He has made it no secret that all creation has been designed to serve the needs of humans and to aid them, be it directly or indirectly.

"If we succeed in enticing humanity to take the path that leads away from the Lord – to walk the path of opposition for themselves – their destiny will also be separation from the Lord and ultimately destruction in Hell. The Lord is Righteous and Just and He wouldn't allow them to go unpunished. At the same time, because of His attachment to them, He will continue to pursue them to the very end, inviting them to turn away from the path of opposition. Herein lies the advantage for us with regard to the length of time the Lord will tolerate the existence of the path of opposition and thus our own existence in this current state of freedom from His lordship."

Impressed by his subordinate's comprehensive answer, Satan addressed first him and then the others:

🛐 This is a truly excellent response, which shows that not only have you made significant progress along the new path but your thoughts and reasonings have begun to reflect much of the way I myself think and reason. For demonstrating that you have aimed to follow my example and to be conformed to my mode of thought and action, I will by no means leave you without reward.

Now, there is one more key way in which we would advance in our existence if we successfully lure Adam and Eve onto the path of opposition. Does anyone know what that is?

⊛ After taking some time to ponder, seeking the response that would most impress the one whose authority was now more than unquestionable, one of the fallen angels, who wasn't a chief but took Satan's promise of rewards with utmost seriousness, indicated he wanted to answer. When Satan gave him permission, he said:

"The Lord has made Adam and Eve to be masters and guardians of the Earth and its creatures. If they leave the path of the knowledge of God and begin to walk on the path of opposition that would lead them away from His likeness – that is the path under our rulership – then they will unknowingly hand over to us their rulership over the Earth! So, while we could not take over the rulership of Heaven, we could have the Earth as our dominion."

🛐 Another profound answer and this time not from a chief! For such an outstanding response, oppositioner, I hereby promote you to chief! Now, the rest of you, feel free to call out any other gains for us in the enticing of Adam and Eve to turn away from the Lord.

⊛ At this invitation, individuals from the group of fallen angels called out several more reasons in favour of the plan against Adam and Eve:

"Adam and Eve are made in the image of God. Afflicting those made in His image is the closest we can get to afflicting the Lord!"

"The Lord has removed our access to His glory and this has caused us great anguish. If we entice humanity towards disobedience and thus to forsake the glory He has clothed them with, they will also be brought into this state of distress. He is attached to them so if we are able to make them suffer, then we will have succeeded in causing Him displeasure!"

"Angelkind is clearly superior to humankind so it is only a matter of justice for us to have dominion over them and the Earth!"

The Plot Against
Adam and Eve

⊛ Seeing that his promise of promotion to the most diligent of his followers was an effective way of strengthening his power over the fallen angels, Satan, with the greatest pomposity, demonstrated his acknowledgement of the angels who'd offered these further responses. He then took a dramatic pause to gather his thoughts and to ponder how to best incite the other fallen angels into executing his wicked plot:

🏛 The reason I took my subordinates through the various compelling reasons why our enticing of Adam and Eve to sin is the best strategy for our own existence, is that some of them here have not yet matured in the way of opposition. Those whose hearts haven't yet been fully immersed in opposition may at times be tempted to shrink back in fear of the Lord, especially when they see the lengths we may have to go to in order to maintain our positions. Recollecting the many reasons for actions against Adam and Eve will be the only way for them to persevere in those moments of doubt.

Regarding the practical execution of our plan, having gone over all that I have learnt about Adam and Eve since their creation, I have arrived at the perfect plot! I recognised that the Lord's absenteeism in rulership is not limited to angelkind alone, for I remembered that, just before instructing the humans to multiply and rule over the Earth, He ordered them not to eat from a certain tree that is in the middle of the garden, or else they would die. And incredibly that tree is called, the Tree of the Knowledge of Good and Evil. If they eat the fruit, they will make their first step on the path that opposes the Lord, the Source of all goodness, and they will taste evil for the very first time! It is then that they will know the difference between God and the opposite of God, good and evil. Then they will also leave the life of servile obedience to the Lord and surrender to the path of self-determination and self-will over which I, the Prince of Evil, exercise such diligent oversight and absolute authority.

☞ Satisfied with the conclusions he'd reached, Satan addressed his subordinates again:

☟ As you can all see, for us, angels, the path of opposition could only be discovered by the most distinguished of our kind, but for humankind the Lord has laid it in plain view, the difference being probably on account of their intellectual inferiority to us. However, the Lord has never communicated His attachment to us the way He has done for humankind, so the fact that He has provided them also with the ability and the path to walk away from Him demonstrates His injustice as Creator far more poignantly than any of His mistreatment of angelkind ever could! Therefore, our guiding Adam and Eve to see the reality of who God is, is also a matter of solidarity with our fellow creatures, who do not have the same capacities as we have.

☞ He thought to himself:

☟ We do not know whether Adam and Eve have been informed of our exclusion from the heavenly host, so we cannot risk speaking to them directly ourselves. Further, even if they haven't been warned about us, we have undergone changes that Adam and Eve may be able to detect, even though it is no trouble for us to disguise ourselves outwardly as angels of light.

☞ It was then he proclaimed:

☟ I propose that we use an animal through which to speak to them. So far we have used animals to communicate with Adam and Eve in situations where direct communication would have been less effective or desirable. As this is a situation in which they would be incited to act in a way out of the ordinary or the expected, it would make them more likely to consider the offer, supposing there is a special reason for it.

Nonetheless, since our removal from service to the Lord has taken away our authority to use animalkind freely according to our own discretion, we must find an animal that will willingly agree to be used by us. It must be one whose characteristics resemble our own – that is, it must be superior in cunning to all other animals the Lord God has made, in the way I have demonstrated such superiority over other angels – and I shall speak through it to Adam and Eve. Only such an animal would see the potential for its own advancement in the animal kingdom once rulership of the Earth has been handed over to us. Therefore, oppositioners, search high and low for a creature that will willingly allow me to speak through it to the humans, to incite them to disobey the commandment of the Lord and make their first step on our path of opposition. Then this life in the fear of imminent destruction will come to an end, and our reign over the Earth will finally begin!

⊛ On this note, Satan dismissed his subordinates, who were now more than convinced that their assault on Adam and Eve was the only way for them to ameliorate and prolong their own existence. Now that they had finished planning their assault against My precious couple, I said:

⊕ Son, the time has come for Adam and Eve's trust in Us to be tested.

ᛏ It has indeed, Father.

☙ Oh, how I wish it could pass them by! Yet, only after successfully passing through this test can they progress in their closeness to Us that We so desire for them.

⊕ The only way they can advance in their ascent to Our likeness is through faith in who God is and who they are in Us. This faith is manifested through obedience to Our commands and rejection of the path of rebellion that leads to destruction.

⊗ Therefore, in the name of My perfect plans and purposes for humankind, I had to allow Satan to go ahead and execute his hellish plot against My precious couple.

CHAPTER

THE DECISION THAT ADAM AND EVE MADE

Final Preparations

☟ Having found the animal that would best suit their purposes in tempting My precious couple to disobey My command, Satan and his angels began to look for an opportune time to execute their plan. At their daily gathering one evening, one of the chief fallen angels reported:

"This evening, I heard Adam and Eve speak about how they're going to be busy all day tomorrow, working in separate places in Eden and outside of it, right until their evening walk with God. Perhaps this is the moment we've been waiting for, Master?"

Excellent work, chief! Tomorrow sounds very promising – they will be much more likely to succumb to our offer if we approach one of them while they're apart. I believe it is better for us to approach Eve, rather than Adam, for three main reasons.

First, after He'd made Adam, the Lord said: "It is not good for the man to be alone." So He took a rib from Adam, made Eve from it and brought her to him. There is, therefore, an internal connection between Adam and Eve so strong that when one day humans have children, their sons will leave their fathers and mothers and will be joined to their wives. What if this need inside Adam leads him to follow his wife?

Secondly, as Eve's natural gift is empathy, she'll respond with an openness and a desire to build a relationship with the animal through which we have chosen to approach her.

Lastly, Eve is more predisposed than Adam to receiving input and suggestions initiated by others and this softheartedness on her part will work to our advantage. This inclination of hers also makes her more prone to seek new experiences and to broaden her knowledge and understanding. It is this natural curiosity that we will appeal to when we incite her to disobey the Lord.

Tomorrow, after Michael and Gabriel have finished their work with Adam and Eve and they and their angels have left Eden, I will make my move.

Decision

Not to Intervene

⚛ In view of the cunning plot Satan was about to implement against My beloved couple, I had to consider thwarting his plans and rescuing Adam and Eve from the impending danger:

☧ Son, oh, how I wish to stop Satan from putting Our precious humans through this temptation!

♁ So do I, Father – just one word from Us would be enough to shed light on his malevolent schemes and would spare them the need to choose between obedience towards Us and Satan's alluring offer... Yet We cannot.

☧ We must not.

♨ We will not.

☧ For the time has come for Adam and Eve to take a step towards maturity; to make a conscious decision not to be led away from Us; to choose obedience over disobedience, Our will over theirs – a bold step towards the love that

228

We share among Ourselves.

⚵ Despite the consequences a decision against Our will could bring for Adam and Eve, the gains their choice to obey Us will bring them, and the joy We Ourselves will have in this, make it necessary for Us to allow them to be tested in this way.

The Temptation

⚶ So Satan was allowed to implement his plan undisturbed. The following day, Adam was occupied to the east of Eden, where he was helping animal leaders spread their communities further apart from one another so that the now larger animal populations would have more space to rear their young. Eve, meanwhile, was in the centre of the garden, working right beside the Tree of the Knowledge of Good and Evil with a large tortoise, whose eggs had just hatched. When the workday drew to its end and the angels whom Michael and Gabriel had assigned to aid Adam and Eve on that day left Eden, a serpent climbed onto a small boulder that was near Eve and Satan spoke to her through him:

⚶ Your work with the animals has been truly fantastic, Eve.

⚶ Eve, recalling her previous experience of angels speaking to her through animals, as Satan had supposed she might, thought to herself that this serpent must have been sent to give her encouragement with her work. She responded warmly:

⚕ Thank you. It does have its challenges at times, especially when I consider the great responsibility the Lord has entrusted us with through this task.

⚕ The All-wise knows you are capable of accomplishing everything He has called you to and, if in anything you lack wisdom or knowledge, you can always turn to us for help and guidance. While we're here, I wanted to ask you, has God said, "You shall not eat from any tree of the garden"?

⚕ Eve looked at the serpent and, after recalling what Adam had told her about the Tree, responded:

⚕ From the fruit of the trees of the garden we may eat; but from the fruit of the Tree in the middle of the garden, God has said, "You shall not eat from it or touch it, or you will die."

⚕ You surely will not die! For God knows that on the day you eat from it, your eyes will be opened and you will be like God, knowing good and evil. You will experience and therefore become able to recognise the difference between good and evil.

⚕ Upon hearing this, Eve thought to herself:

⚕ Like God, knowing good and evil... Heylel said we'd grow to be in the likeness of God and the Lord Himself confirmed it. However, God said that one of the ways we'd grow to be in His likeness is by meditating on His words and therefore getting to know Him better. God is wholly good and that is why everything He has made is good. So if we continue along the path the Lord has for us, we will continue experiencing only good as we have done so far.

The serpent is right – I don't know the difference between good and evil and even if evil somehow came across my path, I wouldn't recognise it for what it is. It is true that

the Lord hasn't given us this knowledge and I wonder why... Knowledge, especially a knowing that would make us like Him, is surely something profitable for us.

☸ Looking at the Tree that was only a few steps away from her, Eve thought:

⚕ The fruit is definitely good for food and what a delight to the eyes it is! If eating this fruit is what will make up for the things we have not yet known, having walked only along the path the Lord has for us, then...

☸ Eve reached out, picked a piece of fruit from the Tree of the Knowledge of Good and Evil and took a bite. At that moment she saw Adam approaching her, returning from his work outside Eden. He embraced her but, seeing the fruit she had just tasted, said in alarm:

⚕ This is a piece of fruit from the forbidden Tree, isn't it, Eve?

☸ She smiled and nodded. Adam looked at his wife standing quite calmly in front of him and then at the bright, juicy fruit in her hand. Seeing that Eve had already made her decision to go against My will and considering the prospect of losing her if he chose to remain faithful to Me, Adam decided to follow his wife. He took the fruit Eve held out to him, embraced her and bit from it himself.

The Immediate Effect of Sin

☸ My heart was filled with pain unlike anything I had ever experienced before. I was instantly overwhelmed by

both sorrow and wrath. Nothing compares to the pain caused by the unfaithfulness of those you love.

As they were eating the fruit, their eyes were opened to see the world and themselves in a completely different way: new feelings began to envelop their senses and new thoughts to flood their minds. The brilliance from My glory that I had placed upon the bodies of Adam and Eve as a visible symbol of their pre-eminence amongst all creatures had now vanished, and with it, all the tangible, blissful sensations that it carried. When Adam and Eve ate the fruit, they lost the confidence, joy and serenity that Satan and his angels had lost at their own fall. However, in addition to that, they lost the state of their inner being that had been unique to humanity as the only beings destined to attain to My likeness – the sense of entitlement to all things pertaining to their growth and development as individuals, as a family and as humankind in their knowledge of Me and their full assurance of My love, care and goodwill towards them. The step they had taken in defiance of My command had now bound the innermost parts of their hearts to the path of opposition, where Satan, the pioneer of rebellion, had set up his throne. Adam and Eve had not only allowed Satan to influence them but, having given him the obedience due to Me, they had come under the shadow of the realm where he had made himself god. The connection they had had with Me from the moment they'd been created had now been broken. From being perfect, they became tarnished; from being innocent, they became sinful; from being rulers, they became slaves of their feelings and desires; from being destined to glory, they became Hell-bound.

They did feel some comfort in the fact that they were

together in this new state of existence. But that was not to last long as they would soon discover that, in losing their connection with Me, they had lost the deep, unreserved and unprejudiced connection they had had with each other. While the way they had related to one another so far had been inspired by Me, My ways and My purposes, they were now to be influenced by those who'd devoted themselves to all things contrary to Me and My will.

Observing the devastating effect sin had had on My creation caused another unbearable wave of pain and anger to flow through My Being. This time, it manifested itself in the physical realm through a quake that shook the Earth's very foundations. Now, all creatures I had made knew that life on the Earth would never be the same again, but none more so than Adam and his wife, Eve, who were suddenly brought out of the illusionary sense of comfort they felt from being together on the unknown path of disobedience.

In the sinful state in which Adam and Eve now found themselves dominated the voice of the one who had first sinned – Satan, the fallen bearer of light. However, he spoke to Adam and Eve not through audible words, but through statements, definitions, judgments and conclusions manifested as thoughts in their minds, imaginings about the world, which their senses now responded to with absolute obedience. At that moment, Adam and Eve looked at their bodies and, seeing them for the first time as strange and shameful in their distinctions and in that they were uncovered, they exclaimed in shocked realisation: "We are naked!"

Those parts of Adam and Eve's bodies I'd designed to be both a visible distinction and a source of unity between them, were meant to be not only the physical fount of the human race, destined to attain to My likeness even before there was a single one of them. They were also a symbol of the beauty, creativity and increase that would come from the united efforts of beings that are distinct and different from each other but work together in a unison that flows from the love between them – a reflection of My own works and ways.

Adam and Eve now not only knew what evil was but it entered their very beings. They began to experience evil. Having realised their nakedness was one of the first signs of this. They began feeling shame, guilt, self-consciousness and isolation. They immediately covered their bodies with their hands, then rushed to the nearby trees to pick fig leaves, which they sewed together to make loin coverings.

Remaining Faithful to Humanity

⚗ I then said:

⚗ Son, Adam and Eve have now made their choice to walk away from Us. Having disobeyed Our command they have submitted to the enemy of all creation. Instead of trusting that We know what is best for them, Our precious couple will now learn the hard and painful way that they cannot experience both good and evil without evil redefining and skewing their perception of good.

⍓ They have fallen! How far they have fallen into the abyss of purposelessness, into the desert of futility. They have covered their own shame with leaves, thinking that their offence has brought calamity only upon themselves and that they themselves have the power to find a remedy for it.

⍦ How quickly their minds have plunged into folly. How tightly their hearts have been bound to transgression. How surely their lives have descended to death...

⍟ Their deed has cast them away from Me, their Father. So let Us go and pour out Our righteous indignation upon their disobedience and, through it, pronounce destruction of this path that We invited them to walk upon: let Us cast them away from Our presence, let Us banish them from the garden of delights and let Us remove their access to the Tree of Life, so that they will not stretch forth their hands to eat from it and live forever in this state of sinful futility. Yet, My desire for humans to be My special gift to You, My Son,

⍓ and My desire to receive this gift, Father, and to lift them up to My likeness

⍦ through My agency and power

⍟ still remains. And it shall remain for all eternity.

An End to the First
Order of Things

⍟ Therefore, in Our judgment of them – their banishment from Eden – let Us do away with the present order in which Adam and Eve relate to Us and to the other spiritual beings by creating a separation between the physical and the spiritual world.

𝕥𝕥 When Adam and Eve leave Eden, let Us, the other spiritual beings and the spiritual world be made inaccessible to their physical senses, so that We and the other spiritual beings become invisible to their eyes and obscure to their minds.

⟡ While We may choose to make Ourselves physically visible to them and, in certain circumstances, other spiritual creatures may also appear visibly to them, humanity's communication with the spiritual world will be otherwise limited when it comes to their physical senses.

𝕥𝕥 As We created humans to be both physical and spiritual beings, their separation from the spiritual world will make them feel its absence in their lives.

⟁ While in their spirits they will still sense the spiritual world, people will long for the fullness of their experience of it to be restored and for them to be brought back to relationship with Us.

⟡ Therefore, humans will seek to communicate with Us through material things and through the produce of their labour.

𝕥𝕥 Yet through this way of relating to Us they will be constantly reminded of their loss of closeness with Us, and their desperate need of redemption from their fallen state.

⟁ It is then that We will declare a new way, which will be the Son Himself, who will one day meet them and will lift them up from their fallenness back to communion with Us through Me, the Holy Spirit.

⟡ Let the Son, the new way for humanity to ascend to

Our communion, bring to ruin the path of opposition – the dominion where Satan, the enemy of all creation, the pioneer of rebellion, has set himself up as lord and god.

🜊 Before discussing how We will achieve this, however, We must first consider how to limit Satan's power over humanity. Through inciting Adam and Eve to disobey Us, Satan did succeed in his plan. Unknowingly, they handed over to him and his subordinates their authority over the Earth and submitted the human race to his power and influence.

🜊 Let Us, therefore, put a restriction on Satan and his subordinates' access to humanity by making it entirely dependent on the human will – whether people will submit to sin or seek to resist it.

🜊 Those who consciously, willingly and persistently live in opposition to Our will and purposes, surrendering their faculties to disobedience and sin, will make themselves susceptible to Satan's influence, even to the extent of being possessed by satanic powers and having no self-control.

🜊 Yet, those who seek to resist sin, aiming to lead a life of obedience to Our will and purposes, will be rescued from Satan's dominion over their lives. Thus, let there be a place where there is no time, where the immaterial part of people will abide after their physical life has come to an end. Let there be a chasm in the midst of that place to separate those who have sought Me and My will while they were still on the Earth from those who persisted in their disregard for Me and My purposes.

🜊 Let the part of that place made for those who sought Us be one that reflects Us and Our purposes for humanity, and let the part designated for those who willingly disobey Us be a reflection of all things contrary to Our character and will.

The Son's Role in the
New Order

✸ Now, regarding the new way We will make for humanity to ascend to Our likeness, while I would have joyously sent You along the first path, My Son, to take upon Yourself their humanity in order for them to be able to partake of Our divinity, they have now exposed themselves to all things contrary to Us, Our will and Our purposes. Taking on their humanity now means that You will experience all the effects that Adam and Eve's sin has brought upon human existence – the misery and suffering of life in separation from Me and My purposes. Yet this is the only way for humanity to be brought back to Us. To lift them up to a life in Our glory now means that You, having taken upon Yourself humanity while not partaking in human sin and rebellion, would be able to undergo the consequences of their sin and be victorious over them. In this way, conquering sin and death, you would break Satan's power over humanity and the world We have given them. I created the whole of humanity as a gift for You, My Son, and You would have brought all of them to Our communion had Adam and Eve chosen Us over rebellion. However, now that humanity has been plunged into sin and futility, not all people will understand You. Not all will value You or accept You as the only One able to redeem them from their fallen state and lift them up to the existence in communion with Us that We planned for them. Yet in the generations to come, there will be many who will flock to You as their only hope for salvation, and their love and appreciation for You

will grow as they themselves grow in understanding of what You have accomplished for them.

We will give You names with special meanings by which You will be known amongst people – names that will communicate to them who You are and why You have come to the Earth. You will be called "Emmanuel", which means "God with us", and "Jesus", which means "Saviour". However, You will be best recognised by a title that will show You are the One whom We have chosen to accomplish Our will for humanity: You will be "the Christ", "the Messiah" – the "Anointed", "the Chosen One" for this task.

On account of My desire for Us to have those people here, in closest communion with Us as My gift to You, My Son, I am willing to send You to accomplish this, even in these current circumstances. Are you willing to go through this?

✝ Father, the hardest thing for Me will not be so much the pain that I will have to endure as I take upon Myself humanity in a world where darkness will have set up its throne. Rather, it is the separation from You that I'll have to undergo as I take upon My righteous Self the guilt, the unbearable corrosive power of sin and the punishment for it on behalf of all who have defied Your holy Name, and all who have transgressed Your perfect righteousness. Yet, for You, Father, and for those who will choose Me, I am willing to go through this experience that will be so contrary to all I have ever known as Your Beloved Son, eternally existent here in Your bosom. Holy Spirit, are you still willing to be the Agent and to empower Me to accomplish this, even in these new circumstances?

🔥 My heart is broken for humanity and I am greatly distressed over the pain they will have to endure. And because You, Yourself, the Only Son, will be misunderstood, rejected and will undergo much suffering. Yet, I am still willing to go ahead with Our initial plan, for I have no deeper desire and no higher task than that which would accomplish Our perfect will for the people We have created for Ourselves.

I will be the One who will, through the ages, reveal Our plans to humanity and help them grow in their understanding of Our will and purposes. I will be the One who will search hearts and minds and will enlighten humans, so that they will see their need for repentance and faith in the Son. I will be the One who will choose humans to partner with Us in bringing about Our purposes. I will be the One who will increase the influence of some and weaken the influence of others. I will be the One who will lift up some and bring down others.

When the right time comes, I will bring the Son into the world and I will empower Him to accomplish all of Our will. I will bring Him into battle and I will make Him victorious as a human. I will make Our purposes prosper in His hands. He will be the Prince of Peace, the Everlasting King, the Highest and most Precious Desire of all nations, peoples and tongues. My zeal will accomplish this for those who put their faith in Jesus Christ, the Son of God!

Judging Adam and Eve

⊗ At this, I made My way to Eden at the very time My precious couple and I would start off on our daily walk. When they heard the sound of Me walking in the garden in the cool of the day, Adam and his wife hid themselves from My presence among the trees of the garden. I then called to the man:

⊗ Where are you, Adam?

🜨 I heard the sound of You in the garden and I was afraid because I was naked; so I hid myself.

⊗ Who told you that you were naked? Have you eaten from the Tree from which I commanded you not to eat?

🜨 The woman whom You gave to be with me, she gave me from the Tree, and I ate.

⊗ At this I turned to Eve and said:

What is this you have done?

🜨 The serpent deceived me, and I ate.

⊗ I then said to the serpent:

⊗ Because you have done this,

Cursed are you more than all cattle,

And more than every beast of the field;

On your belly you will go,

And dust you will eat

All the days of your life.

Then, speaking to Satan inside the serpent, I continued:

I will put enmity

Between you and the woman,

And between your seed and her seed;

He, the Christ, shall bruise you on the head,

244

And you shall bruise Him on the heel.
To Eve I said:
I will greatly multiply
Your pain in childbirth.
In pain you will bring forth children.
Yet your desire will be for your husband,
And he will rule over you.
🜨 Then to Adam I said:
🜨 Because you have listened to what your wife sugges-
ted and have eaten from the Tree about which I commanded
you, saying, "You shall not eat from it" –
Cursed is the ground because of you.
In toil you will eat of it
All the days of your life.
Both thorns and thistles it shall grow for you
And you will eat the plants of the field.
By the sweat of your face
You will eat bread,
Till you return to the ground,
Because from it you were taken.
For you are dust,
And to dust you shall return.
Then I said to Adam and Eve:
In this state of fallenness, you currently see only the
effect your disobedience has had on you two. Yet, because of
your downfall, now creation itself will suffer as it will be sub-
jected to futility and enslaved to corruption. The animals you
so affectionately cared for will suffer because of you and will
turn against you – their trust in you will turn to fear and their
obedience to rebellion. Some of them will seek peace with
you while others will seek your destruction.

❧ I then killed a beast of the field and made garments of its skin for Adam and Eve. While clothing them I said:

❧ This is the first of the other creatures to suffer from your rebellion against Me and these clothes are to remind you of the effect your actions have had on all creation. Many more animals shall be killed in this way from now on so that you can cover the shame of your nakedness and, when you eat their flesh, you will be reminded of the days when you lived as masters and guardians of animalkind.

This animal's life was taken and its blood was spilled to cover the shame of your sin. From now on, you will know that sin always brings death.

❧ Then, as an act of mercy towards humanity, turning to Satan's fallen angels I declared:

❧ One third of you from all ranks of this fallen host are to be locked up in pits of darkness, where you will await the time for the shaft of the abyss to be unlocked and for you to be released. For those of you who remain free to roam the Heavens and the Earth, I have put a limit on your ability to influence humans.

❧ Then came the sorrowful moment when I had to send Adam and Eve out from the Garden of Eden so they would not eat from the Tree of Life I had planted there and would live forever in this fallen state. I drove them out from the garden to cultivate the ground from which they were taken and to care for some of the animals that left Eden with them. Then, at the east of Eden I stationed cherubim and a flaming sword, which turned in every direction to guard the way to the Tree of Life, and it was then that I separated the spiritual from the material world.

While I watched My precious couple walk out of Eden

and thus away from the close fellowship we had enjoyed together during our walks in the cool of the day, My soul was
filled with sorrow, which I expressed in a song of lamentation:

My precious couple: Adam, Eve,
How sweet a fellowship was lost today!
Now you're gone, My soul is grieved –
Why did you turn and walk away?

Now what we had can be no more:
You chose to take the path of sin.
You are not what you were before,
While I am what I've always been.

Despite My sorrow over them, the communion we had
in Eden could no longer continue in the same way; not now
that humanity had descended to the path of opposition and
their hearts had been bound to sin and rebellion. But, during
the time they will live distanced from Me and My glory, their
fellowship with Me lost, those who choose to walk My way
  ✧ will come to Me, the Father,
  ✝ through Me, the Son,
  ✧ by Me, the Holy Spirit.
  ✧ Those who choose Jesus Christ, who is the only Way
to the Father, will ultimately ascend to what I had purposed
for them before the foundation of the world. They will spend
their eternity with Me – the Father, the Son and the Holy
Spirit. All others who reject the Chosen Saviour will receive
for eternity that which they have desired: to have an existence
apart from Me.

Here ends the part of My story in which I have told you how I made humanity to live a blissful, glorious life in fellowship of love and closeness with Me and with each other, and how they lost this life when they chose the path of sin and rebellion against My will.

But this is not the end of My story and their story. Humans continued to live outside Eden and I continued to draw them back to fellowship with Me, until the time came for My Son to become one of them – and change their destiny forever.

Acknowledgements

A big thank you to Desislava Todorova for the final theological editing of the text. Your suggestions, honest opinions and expert advice made a tangible and important impact on the message and feel of the book as a whole.

Hari and Penka, thank you for your hard work and professionalism, for the love you showed for this project and for your gentle spirits that made working with you a true blessing. The Lord's Spirit speaks through every one of your artworks.

Ivaylo, thank you for the fantastic design and for the original ideas you brought. Your hard work and attention to detail can be seen on every page as well as your heart's desire to serve the Lord with your giftings.

Alexa, thank you for your professionalism, diligence and flexibility. You're a true godsend.

Radoslav Apostolov, thank you for the support and help that you so kindly offered at the right time.

Nadya, thank you for supporting us and for the practical help.

Stefan, thank you for the care and for believing in the project.

——— ◻◻◻ ———

Thanks to my mother without whose help I wouldn't have been able to finish the book. Mum and dad, this book is a product of your own hard work – thank you for investing so much in me.

Thanks to my mother and father-in-law for always showing a genuinc interest in how the writing was going.

Antoaneta, thank you for being there "in the beginning" as a voice of strength and for fanning the flame of the vision.

Val and George, thank you for your spiritual support and care that carried me through the hardest of times.

Vladimir and Iliana, thank you for praying with me over this project and for your friendship.

Juliette, thank you for sharing the gospel with me. This book is one of the fruits of your labour.

L. H. Found

———— ◻◻◻ ————

Finally and above all, we thank our God, who through His perfect love and care guided us in this project from the day the vision was birthed until its final completion. Father, may this book be used for Your glory. May it be a tool in Your hand which reveals the Lord Jesus Christ and points to the Scriptures as the source of all truth. May it encourage and strengthen the saints and may it serve to bring many precious souls into Your kingdom.